Haynes *for* HOME DIY

Haynes
THE BOOK ®

ELECTRICAL APPLIANCES

The complete guide to the maintenance
and repair of domestic electrical appliances

Graham Dixon

First published 1991
Reprinted 1991
2nd Edition 1995
Reprinted 1996
Reprinted 1997
Reprinted 1998 (twice)

Published by:
Haynes Publishing
Sparkford, Nr Yeovil, Somerset BA22 7JJ.

British Library Cataloguing-in-Publication data:

A catalogue record for this book is available from the British Library.

ISBN 1 85960 104 9

Printed in Great Britain by J.H. Haynes & Co Ltd.

While every effort is taken to ensure the accuracy of the information given in this book, no liability can be accepted by the author or the publishers for any loss, damage or injury caused by errors in, or omissions from, the information given.

ELECTRICAL
APPLIANCES

Contents

Introduction

Indoor and outdoor electrical appliances of many shapes and sizes are found in every home and each year sees an increase in their number and variety. Some are conveniences, some luxuries and others labour-saving. From the humble kettle to the video recorder, the electric drill to the vacuum cleaner, they all have one thing in common – at sometime they will probably fail to function correctly. That is when you realize what a necessity the appliance has become and how you have come to depend on it.

Mass production and large sales have resulted in many smaller appliances becoming relatively inexpensive. In some instances, therefore, repair may seem neither practical nor worthwhile. There may be a lack of spare parts for small appliances or difficulty in obtaining them. Many of the little shops that were once willing to repair small items have gone out of business, and those that remain are forced to charge realistic labour prices that can make a repair uneconomical to the customer.

Throwing away a complete item not only hurts your pocket, but is further-reaching. Much of each appliance is made from non-renewable sources and the disposal of many items or their contents can be dangerous. With care and maintenance of a product and its working life by repairing simple faults, the benefits are at least three-fold.

● Money is saved through repair rather than renewal.
● The environment benefits from better use of restricted resources. We cannot 'un-invent' electrical appliances to save resources but we can all do our bit in making sure they are used efficiently with as little waste as possible.
● A successful repair is personally very satisfying.

This book's aim is to help you understand how many of our household items work. This, in turn, will help you see how and why faults occur, how to prevent them, how to repair them and, ultimately, how to prolong the working life of your appliances. The book will also help you become more aware of safety through a better understanding of your electrical equipment and its limitations. Regular checks for faults which can be rectified before failure or accident greatly increase the safe use of your appliances. You will incidentally gain more efficient use of your items if you understand their correct operation.

Safety when using, servicing and repairing items is paramount – it should never be compromised. All checking, servicing and repairs described in this book are carried out with appliances completely isolated from the electrical supply. No machine should ever be worked on in a live state, that is, still connected to the mains supply. This is dangerous, not only to you but to others around you – and is totally unnecessary. All checking and testing in the following pages can be carried out using battery-powered test equipment.

This manual has been thoughtfully designed to help you understand the function and operation of the internal components of a range of appliances. Flowcharts, diagrams and step-by-step photographs provide a logical approach to finding a fault and give you the know-how and confidence to repair it. Another important aspect is regular checking and maintenance of your appliances and this is also covered in the individual chapters.

I hope you will use this manual to assist you in the repair of your appliances. I hope, too, that your faults are few and far between, but remember – prevention is better than cure and regular servicing can prevent many bigger problems arising in the future.

Safety guide

Most people have a healthy respect for electricity and understand that it can be dangerous – even lethal – if misused. Electricity at all voltages should be respected. Anyone who does not follow the basic rules of electricity is not only a danger to himself but to everyone around him. Electrical accidents are avoidable: most are due to plain carelessness and failing to follow the basic rules.

There are about sixteen million homes in Britain supplied with electricity and each one contains an average of about 25 electrical appliances. Given the sheer number of items, it is perhaps surprising that there are fewer than 80 fatalities from electrical accidents a year. Although this represents only a small percentage of the entire population and represents only one per cent of the 8,000 deaths each year that result from accidents in the home, the figure is still far too high.

Avoiding accidents

Being fully aware of the need for safety means that the commonest causes of shock or fire from electrical appliances can be avoided. Regular inspection and the immediate correction of faults, failure and wear are absolutely essential. Misuse, whether due to foolhardy complacency or genuine ignorance of danger, can be overcome by understanding and – above all – acting upon the guidelines in this book.

If you ever feel you do not have the ability to do a particular job yourself, then it is advisable and sensible not to try. You can still diagnose the problem because this will ensure that any work carried out by a repair company is correct, safe and reasonably priced. This can sometimes save much time and expense.

DOs

- Do read all the information in this book and make sure you understand it before putting it into practice.
- Do isolate any appliance before inspecting or repairing it.
- Do fit the mains plug correctly.
- Do check that the socket used is in good condition and has a sound earth path.
- Do take time to consider the problem carefully and allow enough time to complete the job without rushing.
- Do be methodical when stripping down an item and make notes. This helps greatly with the eventual reassembly.
- Do double-check everything.
- Do ask or seek help if in doubt.
- Do ensure that a residual current device (RCD) is in circuit when using electrical equipment anywhere outdoors.

DON'Ts

- Do not work on any machine that is still plugged in, even if the socket switch is off. Always isolate fully by taking the plug out.
- Do not use portable mains appliances in bathrooms or shower rooms. It may seem harmless to run a lead from a convenient socket on the landing so that a fan heater or hairdryer can be used in the bathroom, but it is extremely dangerous and must never be done. The rules concerning electrical appliances in bathrooms are strict for good reason: the combination of water and electricity vastly increases the possibility of serious injury or death.
- Do not use mains powered equipment outdoors in rain or damp conditions.
- Never repair damaged flex or cables with insulation tape.
- Do not sacrifice your safety by effecting a temporary repair.

Caution – safety first

Use this slogan as a memory aid for the basic rules of safety when using, inspecting and repairing electrical appliances.

C Consider your own safety and that of other people.

A Act in a way that prevents incidents from becoming accidents.

U Use your common sense and think before acting.

T Tidy workplaces make safer workplaces.

I Identify hazards.

O Observe the rule of safety first.

N Never underestimate the dangers.

S Switch off!

A Always pull out the plug and disconnect from the mains. Appliances vary – make sure you have a suitable replacement part.

F For screws use a screwdriver, for nuts use a spanner, for knurled nuts use pliers.

E Examine and clean all connections before fitting new parts.

T Your safety depends on these simple rules.

Y Fuses: up to 250 watts 1 amp; 750 watts 3 amp; 750 to 3,000 watts 13 amp.

F Insulation is for your protection.

I Do not interfere.

R Renew worn or damaged flex.

S Secure flex clamps and all protective covers.

T Test physically and electrically when you have finished the job.

ALWAYS TOTALLY ISOLATE AN APPLIANCE BEFORE STARTING ANY MAINTENANCE WORK. SWITCH OFF, PLUG OUT!

Plug wiring

Plug wiring must be connected according to the following code to ensure safety. The colours are as follows:

Live – Brown (or Red), symbol 'L'
Neutral – Blue (or Black), symbol 'N'
Earth – Green/Yellow (or Green), symbol 'E'.

The colours in brackets are those that used to be used until the present international standards were introduced and may still be found on some older equipment. Plug terminals are identified either by colour (old or new) or by the letter symbols shown.

ELECTRICAL
WATCHPOINTS

1 **Faulty wiring of appliances**, such as frayed or damaged flex or cable, incorrect fuse, poor socket, damaged plug, or incorrectly wired plug.

2 **Misuse of appliances,** such as using a hairdryer in the bathroom or a power tool in the rain.

3 **Continuing to use an electrical appliance** in spite of knowing it to be unsafe; for example, with a cracked casing, faulty plug, damaged cable, or faulty on/off switch.

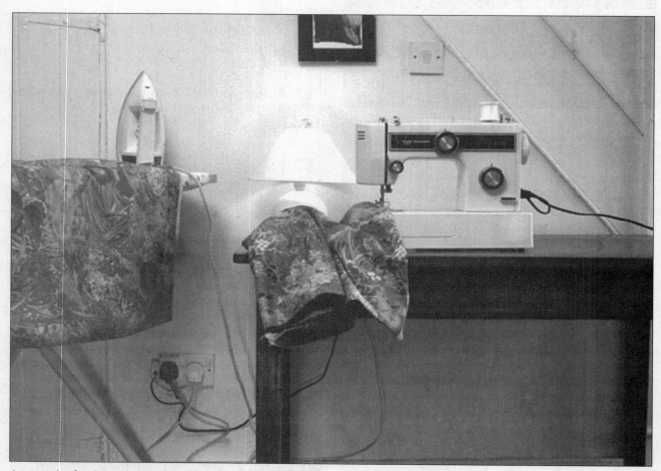

An example of socket and plug misuse. The plugs are in poor condition and the socket is incorrectly loaded.

Tools and equipment

Most of the usual electrical appliances found in the home do not require very specialized tools for servicing or repair. However, sometimes tamper-proof screws or fixings may have been used, such as torx head or unusual tops to screws which do need a special type of tool. These can often be obtained from local specialist tool shops or you can adapt an existing tool from your kit (as described on pages 116 and 159).

Basic kit

Most repairs can be completed with a selection of the following tools: a good range of cross-blade and flat-blade screwdrivers, a pair of combination pliers, ordinary pliers, and a simple multimeter. Most people who are interested in DIY will already own most, if not all, of these tools.

It is fairly easy to build up a good collection of tools suitable for tackling the faults that you are most likely to encounter in your electrical appliances. Most large DIY stores stock the tools you need, often at an extremely economical price. When buying tools, you should always check the quality. Cheap screwdrivers are often poorly made and may soon prove to be a false economy. They may even be dangerous. However, there are many tools on the market that are of a reasonable quality and relatively inexpensive: try to buy the best that your budget will allow.

Remember that the tools you buy are a long-term investment and should give you years of useful service. As with any investment, they should be looked after and kept in a serviceable condition. Always make sure they are thoroughly cleaned and dry before storing them.

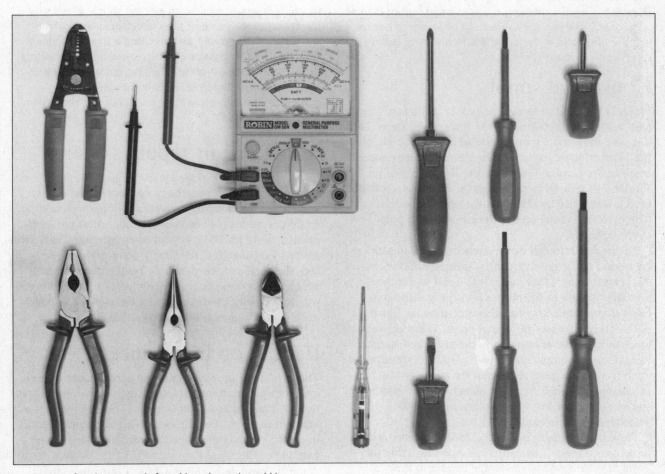

A selection of tools commonly found in a domestic tool kit.

Chapter 1

Understanding electricity
Electrical basics

A basic understanding of electricity is essential, even for those who do not intend to carry out any repairs or servicing of appliances. Ignorance is no protection against your own or someone else's errors and oversights, whether with repairs, servicing or installation. This chapter has been written with this in mind, rather than as an in-depth study of the subject. To be aware of danger helps avoid it and to understand how and why certain safety criteria should be adopted.

Household supply

Power is supplied to an electricity substation at a very high voltage – 400,000 volts – in three-phase form. There it is converted, via a transformer, to 230 volt single-phase for distribution to our homes. In normal circumstances (see Fig. 1), current flows from the live supply of the substation's transformer, through the electrical appliances used in the house and back via the neutral conductor (cable) to the substation transformer's neutral pole (a closed loop).

The neutral terminal of the transformer is, in turn, connected to the ground: earth – meaning in this case, the general mass of the earth. It is usual to use the armoured sheath of the electricity supply authority's cable to provide a low-impedance continuous link back to the supply transformer's start point. There are various types of earthing: connection to the armoured sheath of the authority's supply cable; own earth rod; transformer earth rod via the general mass of the earth; or the increasingly popular neutral conductor of the authority's supply cable. The last type is often called PME – protective multiple earthing.

The earth loop path is a safety device intended for protection if there is an earth fault (see Fig. 2). In this event, it is designed to encourage current to flow to enable the protective devices within the consumer unit – fuse, miniature circuit breaker (MCB) or residual current device (RCD) – to operate in order to isolate the supply to the circuit. Failure to cause the protective device to operate means that the appliance remains live and anyone touching it would receive an electric shock. Electricity always takes the route of least resistance, so a person standing on the ground and touching a live appliance may provide a low-resistance alternative earth path, resulting in a severe shock or worse. The resistance of the earth loop path must, therefore, be low enough to allow sufficient fault current to flow to operate the protective fuse, MCB or RCD.

Variations in supply systems

In countries other than the United Kingdom supply systems may differ from the typical household supply system described here. As detailed in this chapter, various earthing systems may be encountered, one of the most popular being the PME system whereby neutral and earth are bonded (linked) at the supply point to the property. In fact, the choice of which supply system and ultimately which earth system your property has is a matter for your supply authority. However, the requirement of a sound earth path is common to all domestic systems.

Earth loop impedance

The term used for testing earthing performance is earth loop impedance. It involves checking whether the current flow is impeded and by how much. This test requires a specialized, professional meter giving resistance figures in ohms. The maximum reading recommended by the Institute of Electrical Engineers (IEE) is 1.1 ohms for a domestic earth path, unless a Type 1 miniature circuit

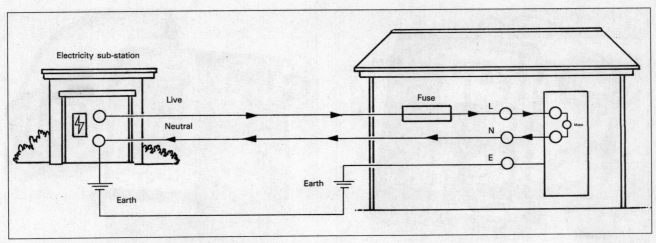

Fig. 1 Typical household supply in normal operation (simplified).

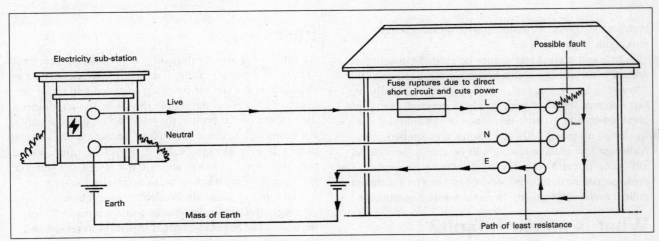

Fig. 2 Typical household supply showing the earth path if a fault occurs.

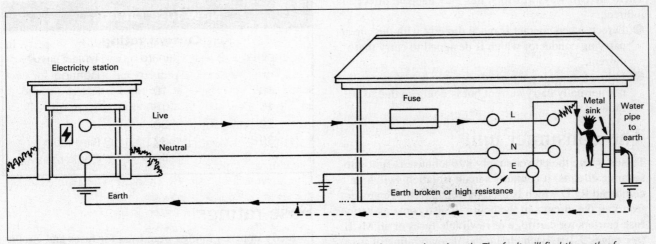

Fig. 3 Typical household supply, showing the result of high resistance or break in the normal earth path. The fault will find the path of least resistance.

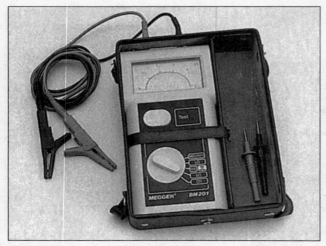

A versatile test meter incorporating 500v insulation test facility.

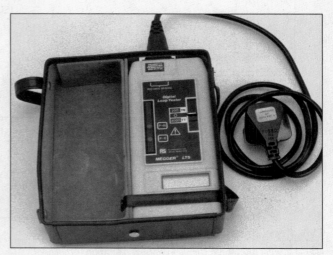

A professional earth loop test meter gives the only true indication of the earth path quality.

breaker (MCB) is in circuit, in which case a 2 ohm maximum is permissible.

A true and correct test cannot be carried out using an ordinary low voltage meter because a fault can exist that allows the low voltage of, say, 9 volts to pass easily (e.g. just one tiny strand of wire poorly connected) but would break down and go high-resistance or open-circuit if a working voltage of 230v at 13 amps was applied. Although low voltage testing will be able to provide an indication of earth path, it cannot indicate the quality. The professional earth loop impedance meter gives a clearer indication of earth quality in more realistic conditions.

What is an earth fault?

An earth fault is the condition where electricity flows to earth when, in normal circumstances, it should not do so. There are two ways in which this may happen: direct and indirect.

● Direct: when contact is made directly with the current carrying conductor which is designed to carry that current.
● Indirect: touching a part of an appliance, that would not normally carry current but is doing so due to a fault.

The consumer unit

This is where the power supply into a house is split into separate circuits. It contains a main isolation switch or combined RCD which is used to isolate (remove power from) all the circuits in the house. It also contains various fuse-carriers for cartridge or rewirable fuses or an MCB (see pages 9-10). Each circuit has its own rating of fuse or MCB and no other rating should be used.

Fuses

An ordinary fuse is a safety device: a weak link designed to break at a pre-set rating. If a circuit is overloaded or a short circuit occurs, the resulting overload will cause the fuse to melt and cut the supply of power. In fact, unless a direct short circuit occurs, the overload on the fuse may not be enough to cause it to 'blow' because it has a degree of leeway over its rating value. It, therefore, offers only a very basic level of safety and will not afford any personal safety as the time taken to break is usually too long.

Two types of fuses are available: rewirable and cartridge. Both have drawbacks and are not very 'user friendly'. The rewirable type is awkward to rewire and the cartridge type, although easier to renew, is often difficult to obtain.

New fuse ratings		
Current rating		
Imperial	Renard	Typical circuit
5	6	Lighting
10	10	
15	16	1mm htr
20	20	
30	32	Ring main
45	40	Cooker/shower

Fuse ratings

Formerly imperial ratings were used for fuses and circuit breakers, but the international Renard ratings have now been added and will supersede them.

Typical older-style consumer unit with isolation switch and wired fuses only.

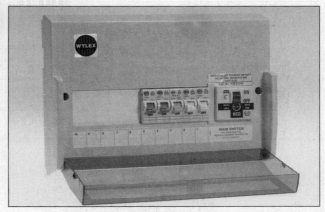

A modern consumer unit with RCD main switch and MCBs on all circuits.

Fuse manufacturers are still using the imperial sizes while circuit breaker manufacturers have mostly changed to the new ratings. An equivalence chart is shown above.

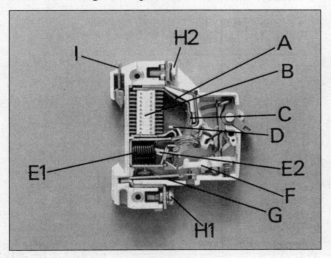

Mechanism of miniature circuit breaker

A	Arc runner	**E2**	Moving core
B	Arc chamber	**F**	Trip bar
C	Fixed contact	**G**	Thermo-metal
D	Moving contact	**H1**	Wiring terminal
E1	Solenoid coil	**H2**	Wiring terminal fixing

Miniature circuit breakers

The miniature circuit breaker (MCB) is now widely used and overcomes all the problems associated with ordinary fuses. It is a small, sophisticated unit affording a much higher level of protection than an ordinary fuse. It is tamper-proof and the unit involved is easily identified when one has tripped (the switch moves to the 'off' position). Most importantly, MCBs cannot be reset if the fault still exists; this eliminates the foolish and highly dangerous practice of putting in the wrong fuse wire or cartridge just to get things 'conveniently' working again for the time being.

MCBs are available in similar ratings to ordinary fuses and operate in two ways (see photograph on page 9). Two fault conditions may arise: a short circuit and an overload on the circuit. A short circuit quickly increases the current flow through the unit. The solenoid coil (E1) , therefore, increases its magnetic field and so attracts the moving core (E2) into the coil centre. This activates the trip bar (F) and causes the fixed contact (C) and moving contact (D) to open circuit. Arc runner (A) and arc chamber (B) act to suppress the arc formed on the contact point. The arc runner draws the arc across the arc chamber where it is broken up into small arcs which are quickly extinguished. The action of an MCB is much quicker than that of an ordinary fuse wire.

The second type of fault, an overload on the circuit, would not cause the solenoid to trip. Instead, the current flowing through the thermo-metal (G) causes it to heat up. It consists of a tri-metal plate that bends when heated. The bending action activates the trip bar (F), causing fixed contact (C) and moving contact (D) to open circuit as before. This operation is better than fuse wire and calibration to higher tolerances is possible.

MCBs are factory-calibrated to extremely accurate tolerances and must not be tampered with and cannot be repaired. The internal workings are shown here only as an aid to gaining an understanding of their operation and, thus, their usefulness. In the event of faults or failures, a completely new unit must be fitted.

Residual current devices

Neither fuses nor MCBs alone can give protection to anyone involved in a direct earth situation (see pages 6-7). This may also apply in the case of an indirect earth contact. The residual current device (RCD) has been

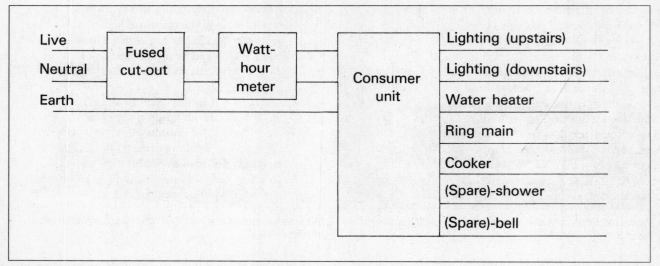

A typical house installation.

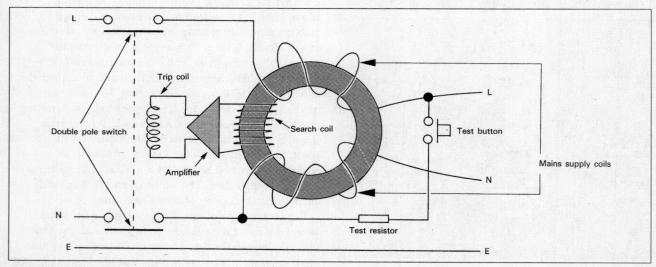

A simplified RCD circuit

developed to provide greater protection. It is also sometimes known as a residual current circuit breaker (RCCB) and, when it was first introduced, it was called an earth leakage circuit breaker (ELCB).

RCDs are available in various forms.

● Mounted within the consumer unit to protect all or selected circuits.
● As individual socket protection.
● An adapter to be used as portable protection and used where required.

The primary protection is the integrity of the earthing. In addition to the earthing, RCDs provide a much higher degree of protection depending upon the degree of sensitivity. For personal protection it is recommended that a sensitivity of 30mA is used.

It is generally considered that an earth fault of 1A or more is a fire risk. 50mA (50/1000 amp) or more risks causing a shock which can have varying effects upon the human body depending upon the value of earth fault current, the body resistance of the person and, of course, his or her state of health. The heartbeat cycle is about 0.75 second. It is vital to cut off the fault current in less than one cardiac cycle. The Wiring Regulations stipulate that for Indirect Contact protection isolation must occur within a maximum of 0.4 second.

How an RCD works

An RCD protects by constantly monitoring the current flowing in the live and neutral wires supplying a circuit or an individual appliance. In normal circumstances the current flowing in the two wires is equal. When an earth leakage occurs through a fault or an accident, an imbalance occurs. This is detected by the RCD which automatically cuts off the power in a split second. Used correctly an RCD is an invaluable asset in any household.

To be effective, the RCD must operate very quickly and at a low earth fault current. Those most frequently recommended are designed to detect earth leakage faults in excess of 30mA (30/1000 amp) and to disconnect the power supply within 200 milliseconds (the rated sensitivity). These limits are well inside the required safety margin to protect against electrocution or fire.

An RCD is designed to sever mains current should an appliance malfunction electrically, or should you cut through or badly damage the mains cable of your lawnmower or vacuum cleaner for instance. It is simply a fail-safe device and should be used in addition to, not instead of normal overload protection, that is, fuses or MCBs.

All RCDs have a test facility and this should be used regularly. Devices used with adapters or sockets, or those for appliances designed for outside use, should be tested before each operation. If failure occurs (does not trip, or trip appears sluggish or hard to obtain) have the unit tested immediately. This will require an RCD test meter and is best left to a qualified electrician.

Plugs and sockets

Problems with electrical appliances may not always result from a failure of the equipment itself. They can be caused by the failure of electrical supply to the appliance via the socket. A three-pin socket must have a live supply, a neutral return and a sound earth path. When a plug from an appliance is inserted, firm contact must be made at all three points. If the live or neutral pins of the plug or connection point within the socket fail to make adequate contact or are free to move, localized heating will occur within the socket. Typical signs of this problem are listed below.

Plug and socket problems

There are various reasons for such problems. They may be caused by one or a combination of any of those listed here.

- Repeated use of the socket, opening up the contact points within it (in other words, general wear and tear).
- Poor quality socket or plug.
- Loose pins on plug.
- The use of a double adapter.
- The use of a multi-point extension lead.

Problem solving

Do not use the socket until the problem has been rectified. If the socket is showing any of the faults described here, it must be completely replaced. It may be advantageous to replace a faulty single socket with a double one. If you are planning to replace a socket yourself, make sure that you understand how to do so before you start (numerous DIY books provide instructions) and that you follow proper safety procedures. Make sure you buy a good quality replacement socket, as there are many of dubious quality to be found. In this instance, price is often a good indicator of quality.

It is advisable to replace all plugs that have been used in a faulty socket because they may have been damaged. It is also possible that a faulty plug damaged the socket in the first place. To continue using the old plugs may result in the premature failure of your new socket.

Plugs are also available in many styles and qualities. While some poorer quality plugs may be reliable for use on low current consumption items such as lamps, televisions and radios, they may be less good for kettles and heaters. Although British Standards still apply to them, quality does vary considerably.

When buying plugs, sockets, and fuses go to shops or

The burn marks around one of the entry points of this socket indicate overheating. Both plug and socket must be replaced.

stores that can give advice and that carry a good selection. This will allow you to compare products. Look for the ASTA mark which proves that the design and manufacture of the product has been approved by the Association of Short Circuit Testing Authorities.

The earth

The faults mentioned so far relate to the live supply and neutral return on the socket, plug or both. Unless a two-pin plug and socket is used, there is, of course, a third pin. Use two-pin plugs only for items that do not require an earth path (see page 15). Although it takes no active part in the operation of the appliance, the third pin is the most important connection of all. The function of the earth system is explained in Electrical basics (see pages 6-8). Products that have three core cable (see Cables, pages 22-23) must have the yellow and green earth wire securely connected to the earth pin of the plug or pin marked E.

Testing the earth path

The earth path of an appliance can be checked easily using a simple test meter (see pages 44-47). Remember, a path of low resistance is required from all items within an appliance that are linked into the earth path via the yellow and green cable.

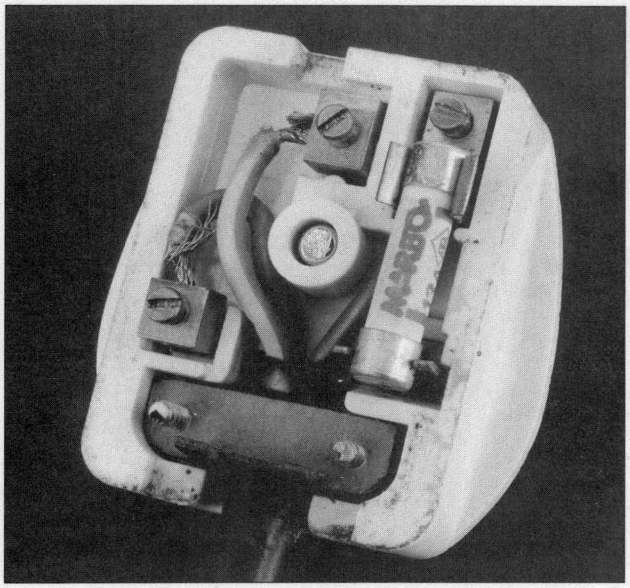

Internal view of severe burn-out caused by poor connection to terminal. A new plug is required and the cable must be cut back to sound wire or renewed.

Incorrectly fitted plug: the wiring is bunched and not trimmed to the right lengths. Ensure all plugs are fitted correctly.

The earth path of an appliance from its exposed metal parts to the earth pin of the plug should be a maximum of 1 ohm (BS3456).

Checking the earth path of a socket requires an earth loop test meter which needs to be operated correctly. This is an expensive item and, moreover, problems may be encountered with distribution boards fitted with an RCD. It is, therefore, advisable to have these tests done by a qualified electrical contractor.

A simple plug-in socket tester, like the one shown overleaf, indicates if an earth path is present, but will not show the quality. That is to say, it may have a very high resistance but would still allow the neon of the tester to light. If the earth resistance is high, this may result in a failure to 'blow' the fuse (see page 8).

A plug-in tester is most useful for checking a socket for reverse polarity. In other words, it will show whether a socket has been incorrectly wired. A wrongly wired socket may still work and give no outward sign of any problem. This is a dangerous and quite common fault.

Plug-in testers can be bought in most good electrical shops and DIY outlets.

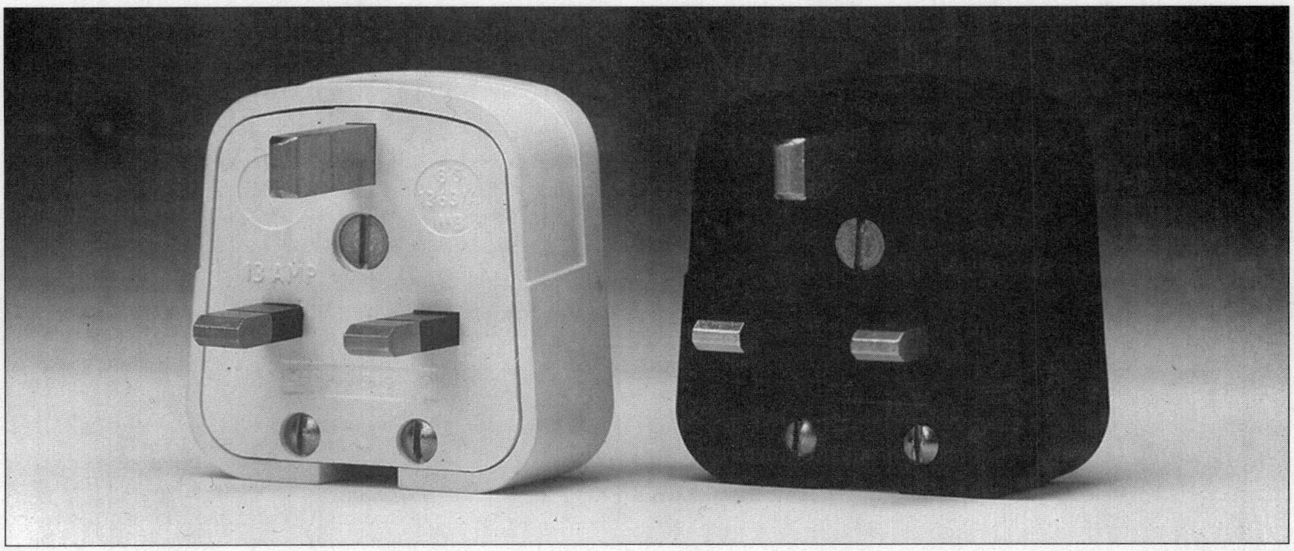

Incorrectly wired plugs and overloaded sockets cause damage and are dangerous.

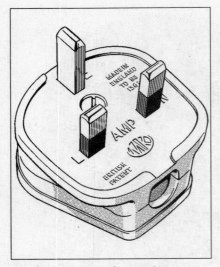

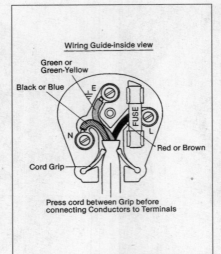

Wiring Guide-inside view

Green or
Green-Yellow

Black or Blue

FUSE

Red or Brown

Cord Grip

Press cord between Grip before
connecting Conductors to Terminals

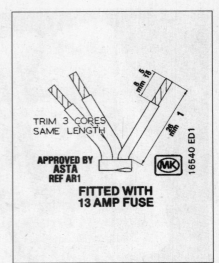

TRIM 3 CORES
SAME LENGTH

APPROVED BY
ASTA
REF AR1

FITTED WITH
13 AMP FUSE

16540 ED1

Specific requirements for MK plugs.

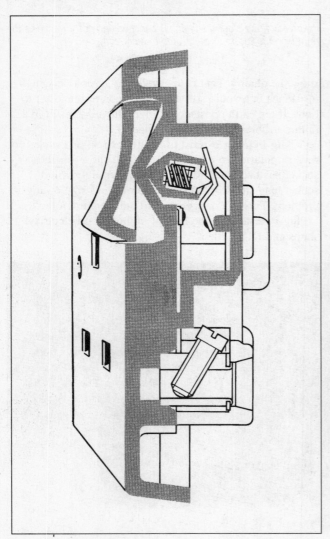

Always look for the ASTA symbol when purchasing electrical fittings.

Internal view of 13 amp socket.

Typical plug-in socket tester.

PLUGS AND SOCKETS
WATCHPOINTS

1   **Burn marks** around entry points on the socket.

2   **Plug hot to the touch** after the use of the appliance in that socket.

3   **Pungent smell** from socket when the appliance is in use.

4   **Pitting and burn marks** around the casing and on the pins of the plug.

5   **Radio interference to equipment nearby** caused by internal arcing within the socket creating spurious radio emissions.

6   **Intermittent** or slow operation of the appliance.

7   **Failure of the fuse** in the plug caused by heat being transferred through the live pin and into the fuse.

8   **All these conditions** are more likely in appliances such as heaters and kettles, which draw a higher current.

The double square symbol on the appliance label indicates a double insulated product.

Double insulated appliances

Not all appliances require earth facilities. These are classed as double insulated and carry a 'double square' symbol on their rating plates, (see below). This shows that the product incorporates a fail-safe system by having no external metal parts with which the user could come into contact. Such products are fitted with only two-core flex when they are manufactured.

Fitting a plug

This is often believed to be a straightforward task requiring little or no explanation or even care. On the contrary, many problems and dangers may occur if a plug is not fitted correctly. Do not neglect this important item.

The information and step-by-step photographs shown here and on pages 18 and 19 deal specifically with modern 13 amp flat-pin plugs. If your property has round-pin plugs and sockets, the house wiring is probably old and it would be wise to have it checked thoroughly by an expert.

When wiring a plug, it is good practice to leave the earth wire (yellow/green) longer than is necessary merely for connection to the earth terminal. The extra length is taken up in a slight loop shape within the plug (see step 5 on page 19). Doing this means that, should the appliance flex be pulled hard accidentally and the plug's cable grip fail to hold, the live and neutral wires will detach from the terminal first, leaving the earth loop intact to provide continued safety cover. A post and nut plug, however, does not allow for this and the manufacturer recommends that all wires be cut to the same length.

Moulded plugs

Some appliances are supplied with one-piece moulded 13 amp plugs fitted to the mains cable. Because of its construction, it is not possible to remove a moulded plug in the normal way if, for example, you need to slot the cable through a hole in a work surface or the plug has been damaged. It must be cut off with suitable wire cutters and a new plug fitted correctly.

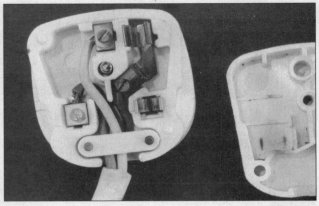

The wiring has not been cut to the correct length, with the result that the cord grip is fixed across the inner wires not the outer heath.

The wiring has been incorrectly bunched into the plug to allow the cord grip to hold the outer sheath.

DOs	DON'Ts
● Do ensure the cable insulation is removed carefully. Using the correct wire strippers is strongly recommended.	● Do not damage the inner core of wires when removing the outer or inner insulation. If you do, cut back and start again.
● Do make sure that connections are the right way around.	● Do not fit tinned ends of cables into plugs (some manufacturers tin the ends of the exposed inner conductors, i.e., dip them in solder), as they will work loose and cause problems. Also the excessive length of exposed inner wire which the manufacturer usually provides can prevent the cord clamp working correctly.
● Do trim the wires to suit the plug fixing points so that no bunching is present.	
● Do make sure that all connections are tight and no strands of wire protrude from the terminals. To prevent this, twist the strands together before fitting.	
● Do fit the cord grip correctly around the outer insulation only.	● Do not allow strands of wire to protrude from any fixing points.
● Do use the correct fuse to suit the appliance.	● Do not fit incorrect fuses. Always follow the manufacturer's instructions.
● Do check that the plug top or cover fits tightly and securely with no cracks or other damage present.	● Do not reuse overheated or damaged plugs.
	● Do not bypass the internal fuse.

PLUGS AND ADAPTORS
WATCHPOINTS

1 **Any moulded plug that has been cut off** the mains cable of an appliance must be disposed of immediately.

2 **Remove the fuse and bend the pins** of the moulded plug to make sure that it cannot be inadvertently plugged into a socket.

3 **Do not leave it lying about** or dispose of it where children may find it and plug it in.

4 **Using a double adapter can cause a poor connection** by the sheer weight of cables and plugs pulling the adapter partially out of the wall socket.

5 **Using a double adapter to run a number of high-current-draw appliances** through one socket causes overloading. Examples might be a fan heater and kettle or washing machine and tumble dryer.

6 **Avoid the use of adapters and multi-point extension leads whenever possible** by providing an adequate number of sockets.

7 **Do not exceed 3 kW load** on any single socket.

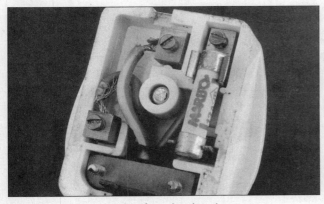
Conductor wire is protruding from the plug pins.

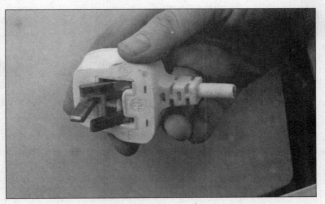
Remove the fuse and bend the pins before disposing of a removed moulded plug.

Plugs and sockets flowchart

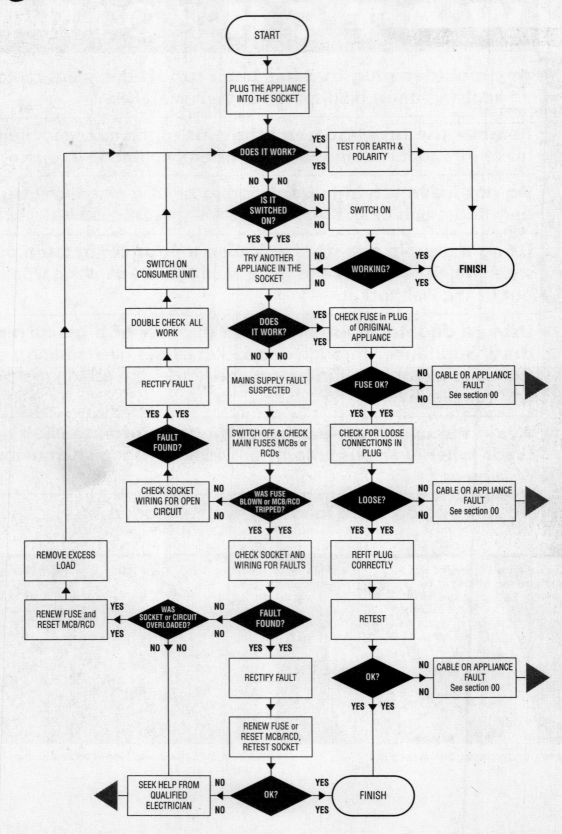

A relay is placed in circuit to cause the phase displacement necessary to start the induction motor (often used on refrigeration equipment). This is a mechanical delay and it is essential that the relay is upright when energized.

Do not confuse capacitors and suppression units. They may look similar but their functions differ.

Speed

When a motor is supplied with mains voltage (now a nominal 230 volts) at 50Hz its speed is a function of the phase cycle (50 cycles per second) and the number of poles in the unit. A two-pole motor mimics the phase cycle and rotates at 50 revolutions per second, that is, 3,000rpm, a four pole motor rotates at 1,500rpm, an eight pole motor rotates at 750rpm, and a 16 pole motor rotates at 375rpm. As variable speed motors require complex stator windings and are expensive, it is wise to check promptly and rectify any faults with motors immediately. A loose motor block connection may allow power to one winding only and cause overheating and the failure of the whole motor. A faulty capacitor or the malfunction of a selector switch or internal thermal overload cut-out (TOC) can also have the same result.

Inspection

When checking for faults always isolate the appliance by switching off at the wall socket and removing the plug. However, the capacitor(s) will still contain a charge. This must be discharged by using the shaft of an electrically insulated screwdriver to 'short' the terminals of the capacitor, ensuring that you are in contact with only the insulated handle. It is not safe to proceed further until this has been done.

If the stator windings of an induction motor are faulty, the motor may continue to run, although it may appear to be sluggish and tend to get extremely hot even when it is used only for a short time. Therefore, if you have been running the machine to determine the fault, proceed with care as the motor will remain hot for some time. If the windings are faulty the unit will have to be replaced.

Refrigerator motor unit with relay.

Shaded-pole motor stator as used in fan-assisted ovens. The copper banding can be clearly seen.

The capacitor

Capacitors used for motor starting may have metal or plastic outer casings with an insulated top with two terminals. Internally the two terminals are connected to two sheets of metal foil with an insulator between. This package of large surface area is rolled into a cylinder which fits into the shell of the capacitor. As the voltage supplied to one terminal is alternating (at 50 times per second), so does the polarity of its connected foil. An opposite movement of electrons is induced in the other foil, even though they are insulated electrically. This causes a delay in the electrical path, and this, in the case of an asynchronous induction motor, gives the out-of-phase feed to the start winding.

The storage capacity of a capacitor is measured in microfarads (mF) and is displayed on the shell. Any replacement must be of the same rating.

The relay

The commonest relay consists of a plastic moulding with three terminal tags, two at the top and one at the base. On the centre section is a wire-wound coil.

The relay's function is to cause a delay in the start winding supply, similar to the function of a capacitor. The main difference is that the relay achieves this mechanically. The wound coil section is connected in series with the run winding. When power is supplied to the motor, the current to the run winding passes through the coil and on to the motor run winding. This current induces a magnetic force in the coil which, in turn, attracts the metal core of the relay. The metal core is linked to an internal contact switch and when contact is 'made', allows current to pass to the start winding. This operation gives the required delay to induce starting of the induction motor.

When power is switched off, gravity resets the relay core.

The relay must be in its correct position and the appliance must be upright for the relay to function properly.

The relay may also be matched to the run winding of the motor so that as initial power draw is high, the magnetic attraction of the relay coil is great enough to attract the core, but when the motor is running the initial high power draw drops and weakens the magnetic pull of the coil.

The core drops and open-circuits the start winding allowing the motor to continue running more efficiently. To ensure the correct replacement is obtained always quote the model number and manufacturer when ordering.

Relay faults

Faults to watch for are: open circuit of the coil, the metal core sticking (in either position), and contact points failing. Renew any suspect relay immediately as, like the capacitor, its failure can subsequently lead to motor failure.

If you have to renew a damaged stator coil or motor and it is relay started, it is wise to change the relay at the same time. This is because the relay itself may have caused the original motor fault or, alternatively, it may have been subsequently damaged by the motor failure.

Shaded-pole induction motors

The shaded-pole motor is the simplest of all induction motors. Only one stator coil is used to create the magnetic field. To start rotation an imbalance in the magnetic field is required. This is created by copper band inserts at the pole ends of the stator laminations, which distort the magnetic field in a given direction, inducing rotation in the stator. Reversing the supply to such motors does not change motor direction as this is governed by the direction of the fixed shaded poles.

These motors do not have a high starting torque and because the magnetic imbalance is fixed, heating of the stator occurs. In normal conditions this does not create any problems although most stator coils are protected by a TOC for safety. If the safe working temperature is exceeded, the TOC will sever the power supply to the motor. Most TOCs are now self-resetting, resulting in constant heating up and cooling down of the motor. If the fault is not spotted quickly, the TOC itself will fail, therefore causing motor failure.

If a shaded-pole stator is inadvertently fitted back to front, it will cause the main motor to run in the opposite direction. Always note its orientation before starting to stripdown.

Benefits of shaded-pole motors are their cheapness and quietness. The drawbacks are heat and low starting torque.

This room heater uses a shaded-pole motor to drive the air circulation fans.

Suppression

When an appliance is in use small sparks are generated at mechanical contacts, such as those found in switches and the junction between motor brushes and commutator (see page 29). This results in the emission of spurious radio waves that can be heard as crackles on radio or television receivers or that are passed down the mains circuit to audio equipment. The suppressor is designed to eliminate the formation and transmission of these spurious radio waves. They are also known as mains filters.

By law all domestic appliances must be suppressed to conform with statutory regulations on radio interference. It is an offence to use an appliance that is not suppressed to legal standards.

Suppressors vary noticeably in style, shape, position, size and colour. Sometimes individual parts are suppressed, but more often the mains supply is suppressed either at, or just after the entry point into the appliance. This is called in-line suppression because both the live and neutral supply go through the suppressor before supplying the the appliance with power.

Faults with suppressors

The main fault is a short circuit to earth (in an earthed appliance), usually resulting in the unit's blowing both the main fuse and itself (in both double insulated and earthed appliances). This is often accompanied by a pungent burning smell. The remedy is the straightforward one of replacement.

Open circuit problems may occur and the unit will fail to allow current to pass through as normal. The suppressor can easily be checked for continuity using a meter (see pages 44-47). When checking, inspect the insulation closely and if cracked or at all suspect, renew the complete unit.

As many in-line suppressors use the earth path as part of their filtering circuit, although very little power passes through it, they must have a good earth path. If an appliance with an in-line suppressor has a break in its earth path, because of cable, plug or socket fault, small electrical shocks may be experienced when the user touches metal parts of the appliance, especially if they are in contact with a good earth themselves, such as a metal sink or worktop. It is essential that such faults are traced and corrected, immediately.

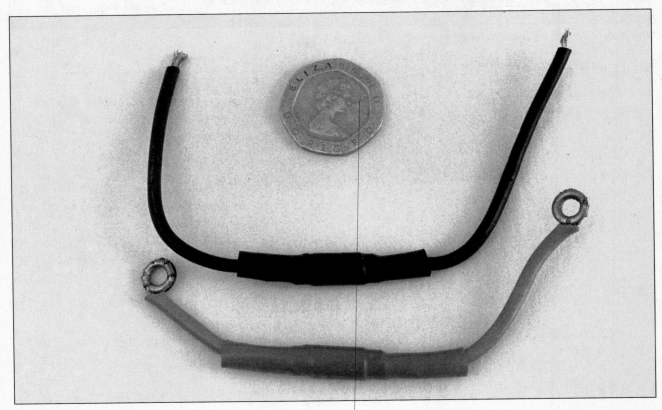

Typical 'choke' suppressors.

'Choke' suppressors

The choke suppressor is an alternative means of suppression, which is fitted in series between live and neutral positions or individually in-line on both live and neutral supplies to individual components. Such units consist of a ferrite core or ring around which the conductor is wound.

Some appliances may also use one or more small capacitors linked across live and neutral to obtain suppression in small double insulated appliances. On some appliances, a combination of different types of suppressor may be found.

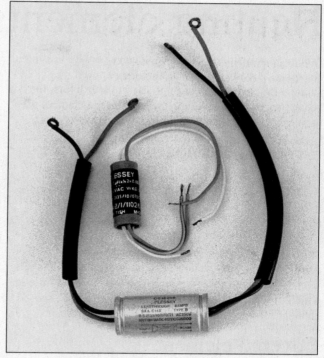

A selection of vacuum cleaner suppression units.

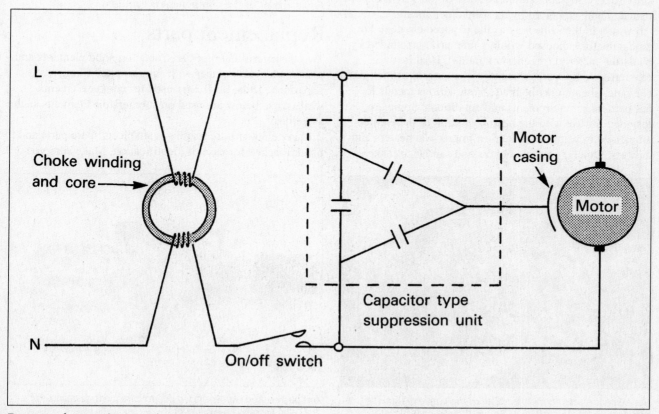

Two types of suppression as used on a vacuum cleaner circuit.

Heating elements

A huge variety of household appliances contain heating elements. The two basic types are the exposed single-wire element, most often used in hairdryers, fan heaters and toasters, and the metal-sheathed element used in ovens, grills, iron sole plates and immersion heaters.

Exposed element

This type of element is simply an exposed length of conductor which heats up when a current is passed along it due to the resistance properties of wire. As it is an exposed conductor, it must be housed and supported in a way that avoids accidental contact which could cause electric shock or burns. It must also be housed in a way that allows the heat generated to dissipate and do the job intended. For instance, a toaster needs a large aperture in which to place the bread so that it rests near the exposed element for it to function correctly.

Covered element

The metal-sheathed or shrouded element can be shaped during manufacture into a multitude of configurations to suit virtually any application because of the way it is both insulated and supported by its solid outer sheath.

It works in the same way as the exposed element, but the conductor is housed within a tube and surrounded by insulating material (magnesium oxide). Heat is transferred to the outer sheath but the current cannot pass. The outer sheath may be made from various metals to suit particular requirements and conditions. Some are designed for use with the heating portion of the element submersed in water, as in kettles, immersion heaters and showers. Others, used in cookers and sandwich makers, for example, are designed to radiate heat.

The temperature may be controlled in several ways. (See Temperature control devices, page 38-41 and sections concerned with specific appliances.)

Common faults

One of the commonest faults is that of open circuit, that is, no current flows through the heater so no heat is produced. This may be due to a broken or loose connection to one of the heater terminals. This then overheats, leaving an obvious discolouration of the connection or terminal and resulting in a break in the circuit at that point. Alternatively, the break in the circuit may occur within the element itself. Test for continuity as described in the section Electrical circuit testing (see pages 44-47).

Another fault is low insulation (see Low insulation pages 180-183). Accompanying this fault is that of the short circuiting of the heater caused by a complete breakdown of insulation. This results in the appliance 'blowing' fuses or earth tripping if it is an earthed appliance. If any of these faults occur, a complete replacement of the component is required.

Replacement parts

Two basic terminal types are found on solid elements and are shown here together with support plate fixing variations. Those above are used for cooker elements while those below are used on submersible elements such as kettles.

Many elements are readily available as spare parts and blister-packed for ease of identification. Make sure you

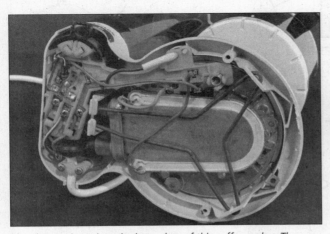
The element is set into the base plate of this coffee maker. The complete unit is therefore required for a simple open circuit element.

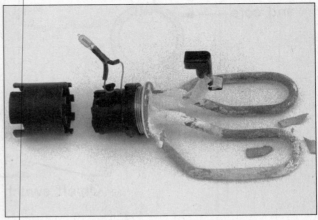
This badly scaled element failed due to infrequent descaling. For advice on descaling see page 88.

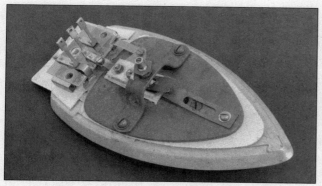

The heating element of most modern irons is set in the sole plate. Older irons, like the one above, had elements clamped to the sole plate; these, therefore, can be renewed separately.

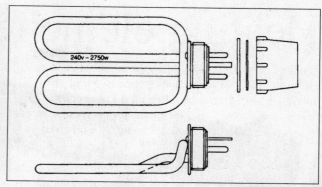

Kettle immersion element (copper sheath, nickel plated).

Overheated terminal due to loose connection on live supply.

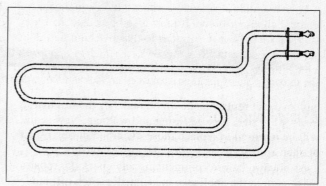

Oven element (mild steel sheath).

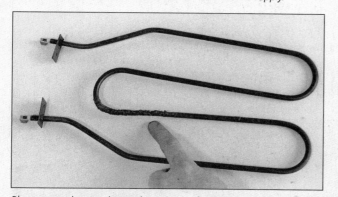

Blown oven element due to short circuit of conductor to outer sheath.

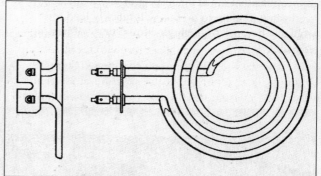

Cooker hotplate (incoloy sheath).

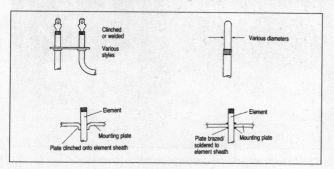

Types of element terminal connection.

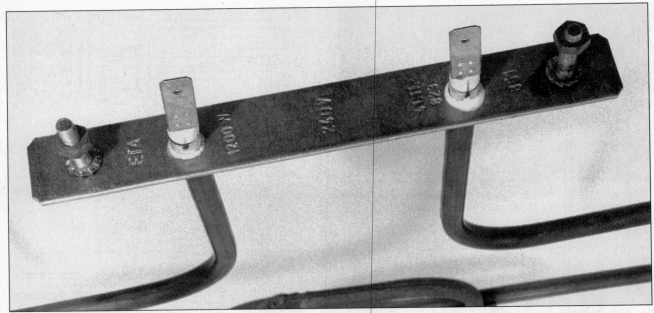

The securing plate on this oven element clearly indicates the voltage requirement and wattage (240V, so it pre-dates 1995, and 1200W).

buy an exact replacement which matches the original in every way: size, type of fitting and wattage. New seals will be required to replace those disturbed during repair of such appliances as kettles and coffee makers.

As always, before commencing any checks or repairs make certain the appliance is isolated: switch off, plug out. Clean all the connections thoroughly and renew any connections that are at all suspect or any that are overheated. Failure to do this will quickly lead to problems because of the high current draw of heating elements.

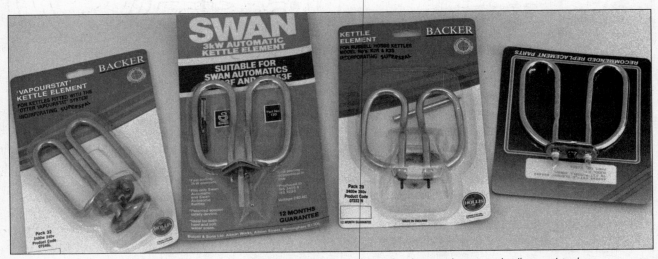

These prepacked kettle elements give a clear view of the shape and fixing along with voltage and wattage details to assist when obtaining a replacement.

ELECTRICAL APPLIANCES
WATCH POINTS

1 **Never tamper with a toaster or similar appliance if it jams while it is still plugged in.** Contact with the exposed conductors carrying mains voltage is possible.

2 **Never use metal objects or your fingers** to unjam or probe the loading area of a toaster or similar appliance while it is still plugged in.

3 **Do not wipe down a toaster or similar appliance with a damp cloth** after use while it is still plugged in.

4 **Isolate the appliance before adjusting or cleaning it**: switch off, plug out. Do this with all appliances, but particularly with toasters, hairdryers, irons, etc., as carelessness with these leads to many incidents that could be avoided.

Temperature control devices

Many household appliances have some means of governing the temperature at which they operate. Examples include the regulation of high temperature ovens and heaters by switching elements on or off and, at the other end of the scale, the control of low temperatures in refrigerators and freezers by turning the compressor motor on or off.

A thermostat is an automatic device for regulating temperature. They range in type from the simple single action switch, which turns off or on at one pre-set temperature, to the fully adjustable type, which can be adjusted within a given range.

The first type is used in a kettle and the second in an iron and refrigerator. The thermal overload cut-out (TOC), designed to ensure the power supply to an appliance is cut off if the safe working temperature is exceeded, may be thought of as a kind of thermostat, although its purpose is safety only. All these devices rely on direct or indirect contact with a heat source and are known as thermostats, or simply 'stats'.

Fixed thermostats

A fixed thermostat will either 'make' or 'break' a circuit at a pre-determined, non-adjustable temperature. Temperature ratings are usually marked around the metal perimeter on the back of the stat. 'NO' or 'NC' are also marked to indicate normally open contact, that is, closing and making a circuit at a given temperature, or normally closed, that is opening at a given temperature. Some thermostats combine both variants.

Thermostats are held in position either by metal clips or by clamps. Make sure of a good contact point and check that the clips or clamps do not trap or touch any wires or connectors. A white paste is often used on the face of the stat; this is a special heat sink compound and it should always be renewed if it is disturbed.

A fixed thermostat operates by means of a bi-metal strip or disc. This consists of two dissimilar metals, with different expansion rates when subjected to heat, bonded together. Heating causes the strip or disc to distort or bend, and the movement is transferred into a switching operation.

The temperature at which bending occurs is governed by the make-up of the bi-metal strip or disc and cannot be adjusted in fixed thermostats. Although stats may look similar, it is essential that a correctly rated stat be fitted.

Fig. 1 shows a typical double thermostat; this example with a 50°C (NO) normally open contact and a 85°C (NC) normally closed contact. (The temperatures do not represent a given appliance.) The latter is a safety thermostat which operates if overheating should occur within the appliance. Bi-metal discs are mounted directly behind the metal front cover of the stat and are pre-set to distort at given temperatures, in this instance 50°C and 85°C. They are linked to contact switches by push rods. Distortion of the discs either makes or breaks the corresponding contacts as shown.

When removed from the appliance, the thermostat's operation can be tested by placing the metal cover in contact with a heat source, such as a radiator or hot water, which matches or slightly exceeds the required temperature. Allow a little time for the heat to warm the stat and bi-metal discs. Establishing the closing or opening of the thermostat can now be carried out by testing for continuity as described in Electrical circuit testing (see pages 44-47).

Check the temperature with a household thermometer and allow a few degrees either way of the marked temperature on the outer rim of the stat. Remember to check if the stat is normally NO or NC. When cool, check that the stat returns to its normal position as indicated on the rim, that is, NO or NC.

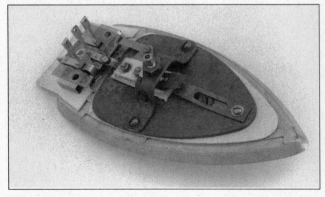

Iron stat in situ.

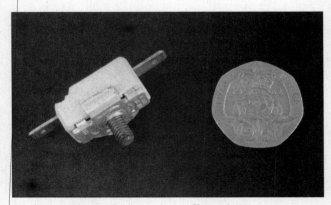

Fixed stat used in appliances such as coffee makers.

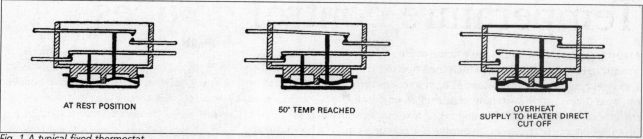

AT REST POSITION   50° TEMP REACHED   OVERHEAT
                                                        SUPPLY TO HEATER DIRECT
                                                        CUT OFF

Fig. 1 A typical fixed thermostat.

Variable thermostats

Fig. 2 shows a schematic diagram of the internal workings of a pod-type thermostat. This type is used in appliances that have a variable temperature control. It consists of an oil-filled pod connected to the switch by a capillary tube. When the oil in the pod is heated or cooled, it expands or contracts in the tube and operates a diaphragm. The diaphragm acts on the switchgear thus breaking the circuit and in this instance, 'making' the other. The cooling oil contracts, pulling the switch the opposite way – back to its original position; the process repeats if temperatures change.

When removing a variable thermostat you should ease the pod gently from its position at the base of the capillary tube, taking care not to kink or pull unduly on the capillary tube itself. When fitting or refitting this type of thermostat, make sure that the capillary tube does not touch any electrical contacts, such as the heater terminals, or any moving parts or sharp edges. After fitting re-check the entire length of the tube for contact with these items. Any coiled sections in the original should be duplicated in the replacement unit.

The iron stat shown (see page 40) is a variable thermostat using the bi-metal strip principle. The large bi-metal strip has one contact point on it. The opposing contact point is mounted on a movable threaded shaft which is linked to the temperature control knob. Heat causes the bi-metal strip to distort which causes the contact to make or break, depending on the degree of distortion required relevant to the movable contact point's position – a simple yet effective means of temperature control.

Unfortunately, the constant operation and flexing of the bi-metal during normal use can quickly tire it, resulting in ineffective temperature regulation. In some cases, a degree of adjustment to the stat is possible and recalibration will often be necessary.

A pyrometer is required if an iron needs to be recalibrated. With many appliances, it is advisable to obtain a new thermostat which has been factory calibrated. Take care when handling such stats as the bi-metal strips can be very sharp and can also easily be knocked out of calibration.

Thermal overload cut-out

The thermal overload cut-out (TOC) is a safety device that is generally connected in-line with the item it is protecting. For example, power supplied to a heating element will first pass through the TOC and on to the heater. If the safe working temperature of the heater is exceeded, the TOC will operate, go open circuit and cut power to the element.

There are two ways in which the TOC can reset when normal working temperature has been reached. The

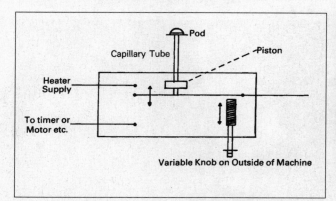

Fig. 2 Internal workings of a pod-type thermostat. In this instance a simple auto-defrost thermostat.

Variable bi-metal plate type stat, often used in convector heaters.

Variable thermostat. Note switches, capillary tube and pod.

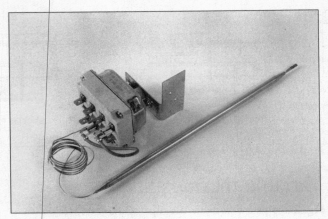

Pod-type thermostat.

simplest is a self-setting version which works on the bi-metal strip principle. This type can give rise to cycling of the fault, that is, constant heating and cooling of the element via the TOC's tripping on overheat and resetting when cool. If this is not spotted and the cause for the overheat rectified, the TOC will eventually fail. This may simply be a failure to reset, or worse, the contacts of the TOC may short or weld together and render the device completely useless.

The second type of TOC requires manual resetting once it has tripped, usually simply by pressing a reset button. Remember to unplug the appliance before doing this and always check for the cause of the tripping and rectify as required. Because this type of TOC cannot reset itself the danger of cycling is eliminated.

The shapes, sizes and styles of bi-metal TOCs vary. Some look identical to fixed thermostats and are housed in an insulated container. In others the bi-metal disc or blade is not covered. Such exposed types can also trip if overload current occurs. For example, if a motor fails to run due to seizing up, current loading would be higher than normal causing the TOC in circuit with the motor to heat up and trip out.

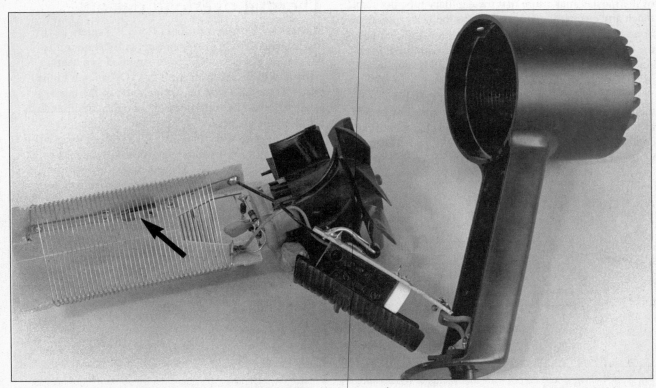

The overheat thermostat (TOC) can be seen set inside this hairdryer element.

Other thermal safety devices

Many modern appliances requiring protection from overheating are fitted with a different overheat fail-safe device that avoids the use of moving parts and contact points that may in themselves fail. This device also has the benefit of being very small. It has several names: thermal fuse, micro-temp and safety diode. Its function is the same as a TOC, but once it has tripped, it cannot reset itself or be reset manually and renewal is the only answer. This type of system provides an extremely high level of safety to many items that, in the past, could give rise to very dangerous situations through overheating. Although small, it is easily recognizable but it may be housed in a protective sheath in the appliance. The outer shell will give details of the normal operational temperature.

   Testing is as before: if safe, closed circuit, if tripped, open circuit. Make sure that an identical replacement is obtained and properly fitted. Crimp-fit securely, ensuring that the new fuse is in the same direction and fitted in the same position as the original. Do not by-pass this item.

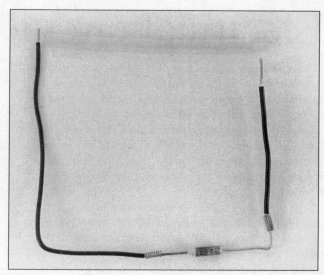

Micro-temp, now used in a wide variety of equipment.

TOC
WATCH POINTS

1	**TOCs must match the equipment they protect.** Although they all perform a similar operation, each has its own temperature setting.
2	**Ensure that an identical replacement is used** when renewing the TOC.
3	**Never by-pass a TOC.**
4	**Take care with blade/disc TOCs** because they can be very sharp.

Electrical circuit testing

Throughout this book, references are made to meters and their use in continuity testing of individual parts of the appliances and their connecting wires. All testing and checking for 'open' (not allowing for current flow) or 'closed' circuit (allowing current to flow) must be carried out using a battery-powered multimeter or test meter. Testing should never be carried out on live items under any circumstances. Appliances must be disconnected from the mains supply.

Although some meters or testers have the facility to check mains voltages, these are not recommended for use in repairs to domestic appliances. Faults can be easily traced by simple low-voltage (battery power) continuity testing, proving that the simplest of meters or even a home-made one like that described below are perfectly adequate. Remember that safety is paramount and in no circumstances should it be compromised. Always double-check that the appliance is unplugged – a good tip is to keep the plug in view so that no-one else can plug it in unbeknown to you.

Choosing a meter

If you decide to buy a test meter, do not be tempted by an over complicated one as it could end up confusing and misleading you. Read the manufacturer's instructions thoroughly and make sure that you fully understand them. The meter shown here is simple to use when continuity testing and has a scale that reads 'open' circuit or 'closed' circuit. It was purchased at a reasonable price from a local DIY shop. The meter will also help locate faults with car electrics, but it should never be used on live mains circuits.

Some multimeters show the resistance value of the item being tested as well as indicating continuity. This can be extremely useful if the correct value of the item being tested is known, although this is by no means essential. Details of how to use the multimeter for this function will be found in the manufacturer's accompanying instruction leaflet. Meters are also available with buzzers or lights which make testing in dark corners easier.

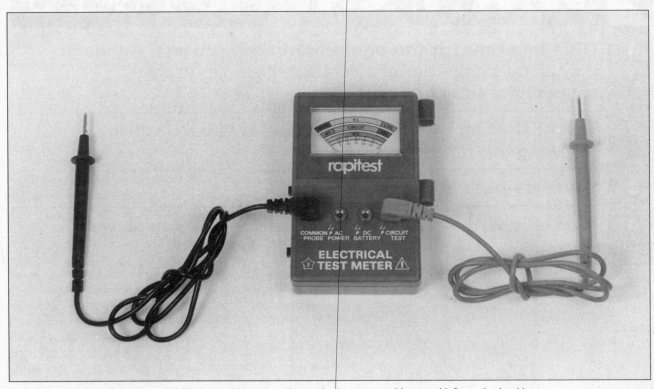

A typical multimeter of the type available in most DIY stores. Try to obtain a meter with a good informative booklet.

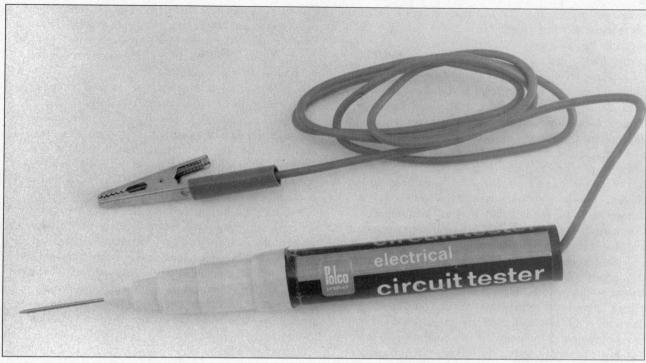

This simple continuity tester was purchased from an automart. It is a manufactured version of the home-made type described.

A simple continuity tester

This simple device can be used to trace faults in most appliances and is very easy to make. It uses the lack of continuity to its full advantage. You will need a dry torch battery, a bulb of the same voltage and three wires (1 x 5 inch and 2 x 10 inch). Connect the short wire to the positive terminal of the battery and the other end of that wire to the centre terminal of the torch bulb. Attach one of the longer wires to the negative terminal of the battery and leave the other end free. Attach the third wire to the body of the bulb and leave the end free.

The two loose ends now act as the test wires on the tester. Press the two ends of the wire together and the bulb will light. When testing an open circuit the light will stay off, and when testing a closed circuit the light will be on.

Ensure that the appliance is isolated from the mains supply before attempting to use a meter. Low voltage bulb type testers of 1½ volts or 3 volts are unable to test the continuity of many components and should be used mainly for wiring fault finding. A test meter like the one shown is needed to test components, such as motors and heaters.

Using a meter

To test for an open circuit in a component, make a note of and then remove the original wiring to that component. If this is not done, false readings may be given from other items that may be in circuit. Attach the ends of the two probes of the meter to the suspect component. For example, to test a heater for continuity, place the probes on the tags at the end of the heater and watch the meter. The needle should move. At this stage, it does not matter if the needle does not reach zero. If the heater is open circuit (no movement), it should be tested further. If closed circuit, the heater has not failed.

Leap-frog testing

Often the most effective way to trace a fault is to use a simple but logical approach. One such approach is called the leap-frog method and can be used to find the failed/open circuit part or parts.

Let us assume that the appliance does not work at all, so we cannot deduce where the problem lies purely from the symptoms. A quick check of the supply socket by plugging in another appliance known to be working will verify (or not) that there is power up to that point. This confirms that the fault lies somewhere in the appliance, its flex or plug. We know that during normal conditions, power flows in through the live pin on the plug, through the appliance (when switched on) and returns via the neutral pin on the plug. The fact that the appliance will not work at all when plugged in and switched on indicates that an open circuit exists somewhere along this normal live-to-neutral circuit.

Leap-frog testing using a continuity meter works as follows. First, test that the meter is working correctly; touch the test probes together and the meter should indicate continuity. Connect one probe to the live pin of the appliance's plug and the other on the live conductor connecting point in the plug. Continuity will be found when the pin, fuse and their connections are all right. If this check proves no fault, move the probe from the live conductor point in the plug to the live conductor connection in the terminal block within the appliance. Continuity should be found; if not, a fault between plug and terminal block is indicated.

When continuity testing flex, move the wire continuously, bending it back and forth along the entire length, so that wire breakage internally – which often causes intermittent continuity – can be completely checked. If this test is all right, move the probe to the next convenient point along the live conductor, in this instance, the supply side of the on/off switch. Again,

continuity is required. An open circuit indicates a fault between terminal block and switch connection. The next step is to move the probe to the opposite terminal of the switch. Operate the switch to verify correct action (on = continuity, off = open circuit).

If this test is all right, proceed to the next point along the wire, in this instance a motor connection. Again continuity is required. If it is all right, move the probe to the other terminal of the motor. This, once again, should indicate continuity of circuit through the motor.

At this point we will assume that an open circuit has been indicated, so go back to the last test point and verify continuity up to that point. If it is found to be all right, then a fault has been traced that lies within the motor and a similar leap-frog test can now be made of the individual parts of the motor – field coil, brushes, etc. The fault, once accurately located, can then be easily repaired.

This simple, methodical approach is all that is required to find such problems. It is best to break down more complex circuits into individual sections, such as motor, heater and switch, and test continuity of each section from live through the individual parts and back to neutral. This may involve moving the live probe that would

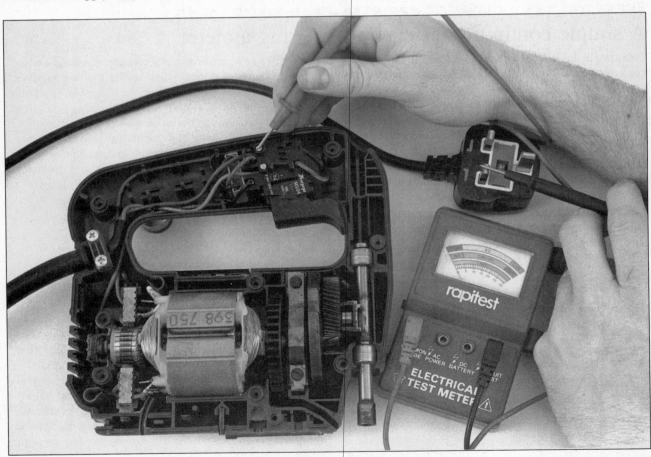

Continuity testing of this jigsaw cable identified an intermittent open circuit fault.

normally remain on the plug live pin to a more convenient supply point within the appliance to avoid other items within the appliance circuit causing misleading continuity readings. With practice, faults can be found even in complex wiring in this way.

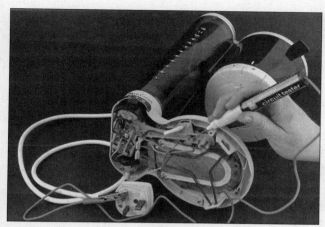

Using the simple tester on this coffee maker confirmed that the micro-temp was all right, that is, closed circuit, so the fault lay elsewhere.

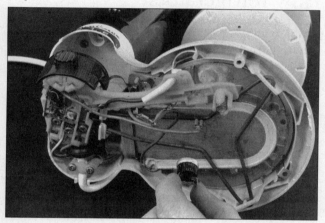

Following further checking of the circuit, a faulty thermostat was found, that is, permanently open circuit when normally it would be closed circuit, opening only at 85°C.

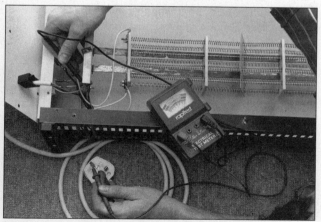

The earth path of this convector heater is being checked, that is, closed circuit. Do not forget that the socket should also have a good earth path (see pages 12-15).

Chapter 2

Kitchen appliances

Refrigerators and freezers

Refrigerators and freezers are now commonplace items in the home. Faults are inconvenient at the very least and, at worst, can prove expensive if the contents thaw out. In addition, most, if not all refrigerators and freezers contain environmentally unfriendly CFC gases for the cooling system and within the insulation materials. Although efforts are being made to eliminate the use of these gases in new appliances, it will be some time before non-CFC use becomes the norm. While CFCs are still in widespread use there are a number of things that you can do to minimize their associated environmental problems.

Regular servicing of your appliance will reduce failure and the need to renew it prematurely – at the moment, probably with another CFC using appliance. If faults occur that are uneconomical or unsafe to repair, the appliance must be disposed of correctly. The refrigerant gas should be extracted and collected in cylinders for safe disposal or recycling. This cannot be done without specialist equipment and knowledge, but local councils and commercial firms will advise.

Even the foam insulation may contain CFCs, so it must also be disposed of properly. All this may seem pointless for one useless scrap appliance, but depletion of the ozone layer can be halted only by taking these seemingly insignificant steps.

It is not possible for you to repair all faults that may occur because expensive specialist equipment is needed for the sealed system. Do not attempt repairs to the sealed pressurized pipework. You can, however, trace, by elimination, and repair many of the common faults found in refrigerators and freezers. If, after carrying out all normal checks, a fault is suspected in the sealed system, it is advisable to call in a qualified refrigeration engineer. A competent engineer should collect any gas that he needs to bleed off during the repair and also use inert gas as opposed to refrigerant to test for leaks. Make sure yours does.

How refrigerators and freezers work

Although there are many different types and styles of appliance on the market, most of them work on the same principle of compression and expansion within a sealed system like that shown in the diagram on the facing page.

At the heart of the sealed network of pipes and tubing lies an induction motor, usually relay start (A), connected directly to a piston operated compressor with which it forms one complete unit. The motor/compressor unit also acts as a reservoir (G). When the motor is supplied with power, operation of the compressor begins. Low pressure gas is drawn into the compressor chamber via tube (F) and compressed by a rapidly moving piston which forces the now compressed gas into the condenser tube system (B). Reed valves are situated on both the inlet and outlet of the compressor unit and operate in opposition to each other by the pressures produced. Heat generated in the compression sequence and any that has been absorbed from the sealed motor is dissipated in the condenser matrix (B). This cooling allows the refrigerant gas to liquefy. The liquefied gas then passes through a dryer/filter (C) designed to remove any traces of water vapour or crystals prior to passing through a capillary tube (small bore) and on to the evaporator. A small-bore capillary tube is used to control the flow of liquid to the evaporator. When the high pressure liquid gas from the capillary tube enters the large network of the evaporator (E) the sudden expansion of the liquefied gas results in dramatic cooling of the unit as the liquid reverts to a lower pressure gas again.

Being a sealed system, this is a continuous operation as long as the motor and compressor unit run, the system remains sealed and there is enough gas within the system. The tube (H) is used to evacuate the system during

High-pressure gas

High-pressure liquid

Low-pressure liquid

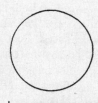

Low-pressure gas

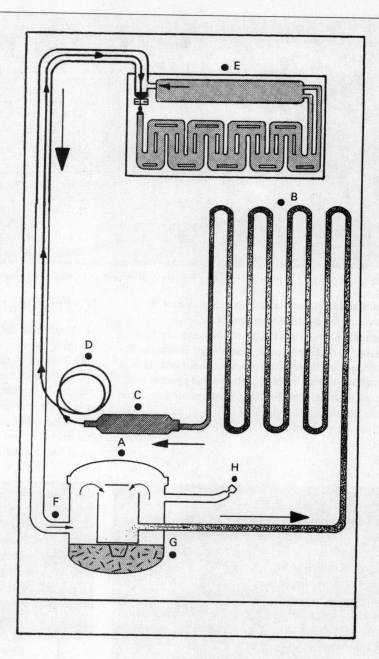

Sealed refrigeration system
A Induction motor
B Condenser matrix
C Dryer/filter
D Capillary tube
E Evaporator
F Tube
G Reservoir
H Evacuation tube

Internal view of refrigerator compartment showing the evaporation unit and drainage channel below for auto-defrost.

manufacture and to introduce the coolant gas then or during servicing by qualified personnel.

Most systems allow for a length of the capillary tube from the filter to be fixed on the outside (or inside on some machines) of the return from the evaporator. This is done to improve the efficiency of the sealed system and keeps the return tube from forming condensation because it is colder than the surrounding air.

Refrigerator auto defrost

The automatic defrost operation is done simply by warming the evaporator area by means of a small heater unit. This melts the build-up of ice particles which run off the base of the unit into a catchment channel. The channel is designed to funnel the liquid through a small hole in the rear of the appliance on to a dished area on top of the compressor unit. The heat generated by the normal operation of the compressor/motor unit causes the small but regular amount of water to evaporate into the

The internal view of this freezer section shows the evaporator unit forms two of the shelves in this model (in common with several other makes), and in this instance requires defrosting.

This rear view of a refrigerator unit clearly shows the motor/compressor unit in the base and the condenser matrix above.

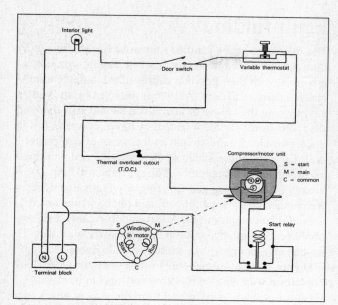

A simple refrigerator circuit

atmosphere. The switching of the heater unit is linked to the thermostat operation, working in opposition to the cooling sequence.

The small hole from the collection channel to the exterior dish mounted on the compressor/motor unit can easily block, causing water to accumulate in the base of the refrigerator. This may mislead you into thinking the appliance has a serious fault. Periodically check that the vent hole and channels are free from debris. This hole can be cleared with a pipe cleaner or similar flexible object.

Temperature control

The temperature in refrigerators and freezers is governed by a simple thermostat arrangement. Variable capillary thermostats are used by nearly all manufacturers and replacement units are generally available. When replacing a thermostat, make sure you buy one identical to the original. It is advisable to fit the new unit on a one-to-one basis. As with all repairs, ensure the appliance is isolated (switch off, plug out) before checks or repairs are carried out.

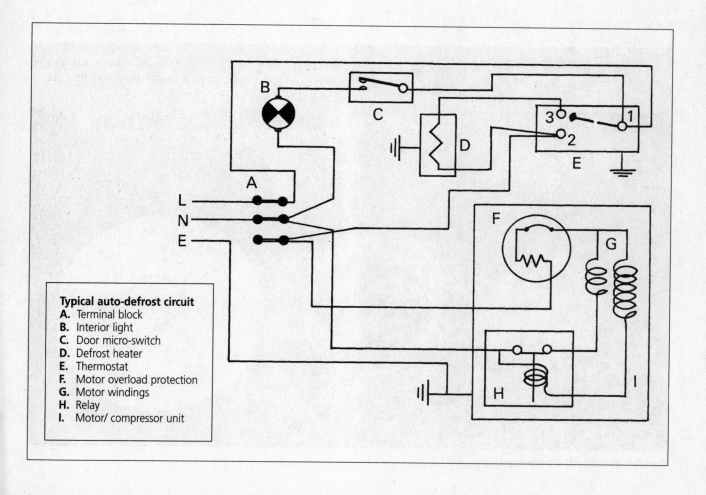

Typical auto-defrost circuit
A. Terminal block
B. Interior light
C. Door micro-switch
D. Defrost heater
E. Thermostat
F. Motor overload protection
G. Motor windings
H. Relay
I. Motor/ compressor unit

Frost free systems

This system does not produce an ice build-up during the refrigeration or freezing process. Cooling is by compression and expansion with the addition of a motorized fan which circulates the air throughout the compartments to give a more even distribution of cold air. The system includes a means of dehumidifying the air (it condenses on the coldest part of the system and then is drained away to evaporate outside the load compartment). This is a simple operation that works extremely well.

Any likely mechanical and electrical problems will be much the same as with conventional appliances with the addition of possible faults with the circulation fan and motor.

Although faults associated with excess frost build-up are eliminated with this system, the running cost and the initial purchase price are higher.

Fault finding

The following pages list the faults most likely to occur in both refrigerators and freezers. Seven general symptoms are given with their possible causes listed in descending order according to how likely they are. Next to the causes are notes on the course of action you should take to avoid the faults or rectify them once they have occurred.

Regular checks and simple maintenance of equipment will make you more aware of the operation and workings of your particular appliance. This, in turn, will help greatly in diagnosing and isolating any faults that occur. Remember safety is paramount and in no circumstances should it be compromised. Always double-check that the appliance is unplugged. Keep the plug in view so that no-one else can plug it in without your knowing.

Do not jump to instant conclusions and start work in a haphazard way. Sit down calmly and start to work out what the problem may be and form the plan of attack in a logical and concise manner.

Typical thermostat kit now widely available.

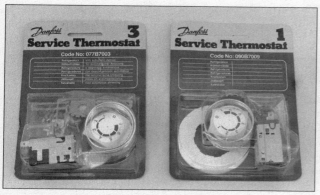

Various types of thermostats are available; make sure that you buy a replacement which matches the original.

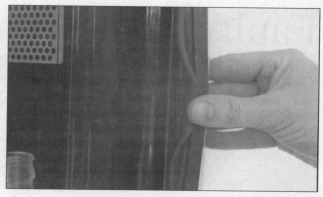

Check door seals regularly for signs of wear, cracks or splitting and renew if suspect. Adjust the door if it is out of position.

FREEZER
WATCH POINTS

1 **Check all the seals around the door.** Renew split or poor seals immediately.

2 **Do not leave the door open for long periods at a time,** as moisture in the atmosphere will condense on the cold interior.

3 **Read the defrosting instructions.** Only some appliances defrost automatically.

4 **Check regularly that the vent hole and channel** on auto-defrost models are clear.

5 **Clean the interior** with a recognized refrigerator/ freezer interior cleaner or a weak solution of bicarbonate of soda, rinsed off with lukewarm water.

6 **Make sure that the appliance stands as level as possible** (most have adjustable feet) and that it does not rock.

Fault finder

Symptom: Load compartment temperature too high	
POSSIBLE CAUSES	**ACTION**
Thermostat set at wrong temperature.	Check setting required for contents.
Door left open for too long.	Avoid doing this.
Door twisted/door seal faulty.	Adjust or renew as required.
Evaporator needs defrosting/excessive icing of evaporator unit.	This will not occur with regular defrosting or on auto-defrost models. Heat pod/stat suspect. Check and renew if required.
Too many items for freezing down.	Do not exceed the freeze-down capability of your appliance. Refer to the manufacturer's instruction book for details.
Overloaded cabinet.	Check setting required for contents. Avoid doing this.
Appliance sited too near a heat source.	Avoid this situation; reposition the appliance.
Room temperature high. Appliance running continually to maintain correct internal temperature.	Check operation when room temperature returns to normal.
Start relay or TOC nuisance- tripping, failing during normal use.	Renew as required.
Restriction within the capillary tube.	Checking requires a trained engineer. Check and eliminate other possible causes first.
Faulty compressor/motor unit.	Checking requires a trained engineer. Check and eliminate other possible causes first.
Leakage of or too little refrigerant gas.	Checking requires a trained engineer. Check and eliminate other possible causes first.

Symptom: Unit runs continuously or for very long periods but achieves no cooling at all	
POSSIBLE CAUSES	**ACTION**
Leakage of or too little refrigerant gas.	Checking requires a trained engineer. Check and eliminate other possible causes first.
Pipe work blocked. Moisture, dirt or kink in matrix.	Checking requires a trained engineer. Check and eliminate all other possible causes first.
Faulty compressor unit.	Checking requires a trained engineer. Check and eliminate other possible causes first.

Symptom: Load compartment temperature too low

POSSIBLE CAUSES	ACTION
Fast freeze switch left on (if fitted)	Reset switch.
Thermostat at wrong temperature.	Check setting required for contents.
Faulty thermostat switch.	See Temperature control devices (pages 40-43).
Contacts on fast freeze switch stuck in the 'on' position.	Isolate. Check switch and renew if required. See Electrical circuit testing (page 44-47).
Thermostat capillary tube out of position.	Check. Reposition as required.
Broken thermostat capillary tube.	See Temperature control devices (pages 40-43)
Solenoid valve (only on appliance with two-load compartments and fitted with only one compressor).	Some appliances use one compressor for two load compartments via a valve which alternates cooling between refrigerator and freezer via the thermostats.
Faulty defrost heater (auto-defrost models)	Heat pod or thermostat suspect. Check and renew if required.

Symptom: Unit runs continuously for long period with only partial cooling

POSSIBLE CAUSES	ACTION
Light does not switch off when door is closed.	Micro switch or actuating arm sticking. Isolate and test. Heat from bulb causes warming of the interior, hence the continual running or frequent cycling.
Very high room temperature.	Check when room temperature returns to normal.
Door left open for long periods or faulty door seal.	Close door or renew seals as necessary.
Overloaded refrigerator or freezer.	Avoid loading too much at any one time.
Faulty valve in compressor unit.	Some appliances use one compressor for two load compartments via a valve which alternates cooling between refrigerator and freezer via the thermostats.
Loss or shortage of refrigerant gas.	Checking requires a trained engineer. Check and eliminate all other possible causes first.
Partial restriction in system.	Checking requires a trained engineer. Check and eliminate all other possible causes first.

Fault finder

Symptom: Compressor/motor unit fails to start/run

POSSIBLE CAUSES	ACTION
No power from wall socket.	Check house fuse. See Safety guide (pages 2-4) and Plugs and sockets (pages 12-21).
Faulty thermostat.	See Temperature control devices (pages 40-43).
Faulty start relay or overload protector.	See Motors (page 28-33). Renew as required.
Open circuit or shorted wiring harness.	See The wiring harness (pages 26-27).
Faulty or burnt out compressor windings.	See Motors (pages 28-33).
Seized compressor – mechanical.	Checking and rectification requires a trained engineer.
Insufficient ventilation for condenser causing the compressor/motor unit to overheat and trip the TOC.	Adjust position to allow airflow.
Extremely low room temperature (below freezing).	No need for appliance to operate.

Symptom: Symptom: Intermittent TOC operation when motor starts (nuisance tripping)

POSSIBLE CAUSES	ACTION
Faulty thermostat.	See Temperature control devices (pages 40-43). Renew if required.
Faulty start relay or overload protector.	See Motors (pages 28-33). Renew if required.
Faulty motor compressor.	This requires a trained engineer. Eliminate all other possible causes first.
Restriction within the capillary tube.	Inspect capillary tube for kinks. Internal faults require a trained engineer.
Overloaded cabinet.	Avoid loading too much at any one time.

Symptom: Load compartment odours

POSSIBLE CAUSES	ACTION
Appliance stored/left switched off for long time with door closed.	Always store appliances with door left slightly ajar to allow air to circulate around the interior.
Unclean load compartment.	Clean interior regularly.
Uncovered foodstuffs.	Cover strong-smelling foodstuffs when storing.

Renewing the thermostat

TOOLS AND MATERIALS

☐ Screwdriver
☐ Continuity meter
☐ Thermostat

1 Ensure the appliance is isolated before commencing any repair or servicing: switch off, plug out.

2 The fault with this refrigerator is that it continually runs and will not regulate temperature. The fault has been traced to a broken capillary tube on the thermostat behind the evaporator plate.

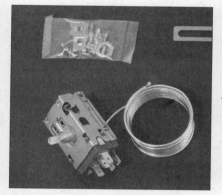

3 A new thermostat is checked for compatibility before fitting.

4 To remove the old thermostat, ease the selector knob off the shaft (push fit only in this instance). Remove the bulb cover and bulb to render the securing screw on the rear accessible.

Refitting is a reversal of the removal procedure. Take care to ensure that all the capillary tubes and wiring are refitted as they were originally and all covers are repositioned correctly. Earth continuity tests should be done before functional testing via an RCD protected supply.

5 Remove the securing screw and carefully ease the cover from its position to expose the thermostat. Make a note of the wiring before removal.

6 The end of the capillary tube is secured to the evaporator by means of a plastic clip and is easily removed. Note the way in which the tube is fitted.

Fridge/Freezer noise diagnosis flowchart

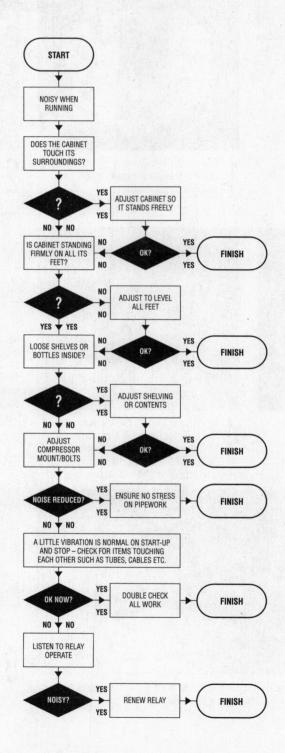

Hobs and ovens

These are among the most frequently used items in the home. Generally, they are very reliable, but when a problem does occur, it is usually at the most inconvenient time. Over the years, ovens and hobs have become increasingly complex with the addition of digital timers, touch controls and other refinements. However, many still function with parts that have changed little from their predecessors' and it is these appliances that are covered in the following pages.

It is essential to remember that these appliances are connected directly to the mains supply and, as with any repair, cleaning or service, must be completely isolated. In this instance, the main double-pole isolation switch for the appliance must be switched off and also the fuse for the cooker/hob circuit removed from the main distribution board. If an MCB is fitted in place of a fuse, ensure it is in the off position. Do not proceed with any repair or service if both these requirements are not met and also make sure you advise others who may use the switch of your intentions.

Hob elements

The hob works by means of heating elements (usually four). These can be of various patterns and may be either

Check hob element closely for signs of failure.

double or single operation. The fixing plate on the element gives details of wattage, and a simple inspection of the element will determine size and style – double or single and number of turns or rings the element has.

Continuity testing is simple (see Heating elements, pages 36-39 and Electrical circuit testing, pages 44-47). If a replacement is required, it is essential that all the relevant criteria of the old element be met by the new one, that is, wattage, size, number of turns, etc. Some elements are sold as separate items, while others come complete with their own dished recess. The latter are normally the type of element that can be tilted or swivelled for cleaning purposes.

As with all heaters, it is most important that the push-on or screw-on connections to the element are fitted securely and all cables and covers are sound. The cable used within the appliance is heat resistant and shrouded for protection. Make sure all cable runs are routed correctly and not trapped or allowed to foul sharp or hot surfaces. All metal parts must be part of the earth path and the appliance must be earthed in accordance with the manufacturer's instructions (see Safety guide, pages 2-4).

When a replacement element is required, it may be possible to fit an economizer element. These are available in most of the popular sizes and are completely interchangeable. The fitting of such elements in place of the standard type can result in a saving of up to 10 per cent in consumption.

Temperature control

The more popular hobs use spiral radiant elements in either double or single form. Temperature control is by means of an energy regulator. Manufacturers may use different wattages, sizes and styles (double or single) of element, so it is essential that only the correct replacement is obtained and fitted. They are widely available, but do make sure you obtain one of the highest quality.

Make a note of all wiring positions and routes before removal. Some replacement controls are sold with sticky labels for the purpose of marking the wiring. This is especially helpful with older appliances where the new unit may have a different wiring configuration as a result of improvements in switch design and operation.

The function of the regulator is simply to turn the supply voltage to the element on and off periodically. The temperature variation is, therefore, in direct proportion to the rate of the on/off sequence, which is controlled by means of a bi-metal strip. Within the unit is a large

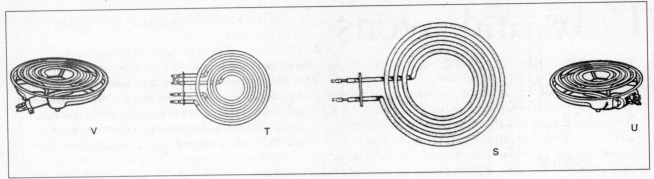

Types of hob element: Single four-turn (S) Double element (T) Lift-up type (U) Swivel-type element (V).

bi-metal plate with a small heating element secured to it. On early regulators a small wound element was used and open-circuit faults were common. The new control, shown here, uses a thick-film resistor to heat the bi-metal plate and prevents problems associated with the earlier type. The control includes a switching action at the 'off' position. When turned on, the live contact is allowed to rest on a cam linked to the shaft of the unit. The cam varies the distance required for the bi-metal to move before operation of this switch takes place, that is, the more deflection required, the longer power is supplied to the element. When the bi-metal plate has moved enough to cause the switch to go open circuit, thus removing power from the element, the same switching action removes the supply to the small element/resistor, allowing the bi-metal plate to cool and reset the switch. This process repeats for as long as the switch is in the 'on' position. The varying lift of the cam is proportional to the visual heat setting indication on the hob switch control panel: low, medium and high.

Checking a hob control

The information given here also applies to the grills on many cookers. This is a simple way to ascertain if the control is faulty. Short circuit failures on elements may damage regulators in which case, if you are in any doubt, renew it.

The following test is for a single circuit application, that is, a single element. For double regulators, that is, a double element, the same procedure will be required on both single and double operations of the switch. From off position an anticlockwise turn will put into circuit one element (usually the inner), a clockwise turn from the off position will put into circuit both inner and outer. Check that double regulators operate independently on a half turn each. For singles, use ony a full turn.
- Switch off the power to the hob by means of the mains switch.
- Rotate the knob slowly clockwise from 'off'. A click

Internal view of regulator showing switch contacts, cam and internal heater on bi-metal strip.

Typical energy regulator.

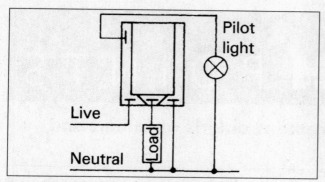

Typical wiring circuit for regulator (grill or hotplate).

should be heard when the knob is at 'on' or at the lowest mark on the dial. The thermal switch is now made.

● Return to 'off' by slowly rotating the knob anticlockwise. A click should be heard before the 'off' position is reached. The thermal switch is now broken.

● Ensure that the knob is left in the 'off' position.

● Switch on the power to the hob by means of the mains switch.

● Turn the knob slowly clockwise until the click is heard and leave the knob in this position. The switch should break with a further audible click in approximately 5-10 seconds. If there have been no further clicks after 5-10 seconds and the heating element remains full on, the regulator must be considered faulty and should be replaced. If there is a pilot light, it should remain illuminated during this check.

● Turn the knob to position 3. At this position 'on' and 'off' times will be approximately equal, and clicks will be heard at intervals of approximately 10-25 seconds.

● Turn the knob to the 'full' position. The hotplate

which is controlled by this regulator will glow red-hot after just a few minutes.

● Take care to avoid the elements during this test sequence. If the above checks prove negative, that is to say, the control appears to be functioning correctly, the element should be checked (see Heating elements, pages 36-39). If a fault is found in either the control or the element, do not attempt adjustment as only renewal of the unit concerned is possible.

Ovens

The temperature in an oven is regulated by a pod-type thermostat which allows the high degree of temperature variation required for the oven to function correctly. (The operation of a variable thermostat is described in Temperature control devices, see pages 40-43.) Heating is by radiant elements, the size, shape and wattage of which vary enormously between makes and individual models. It is therefore essential that any replacement part matches the original in every way.

The two most commonly used ovens today are the conventional oven, which has two or more elements situated either at the sides or top and bottom of the oven (usually behind the oven's inner lining), and the fan oven, which usually consists of one circular element that surrounds or is positioned in front of a fan driven by a shaded-pole motor (see Motors, page 26-31). The air system provides uniform heat distribution within the oven.

Element failure is not uncommon in both versions of ovens because of heavy usage. Generally, repairs to the oven are not particularly difficult, although access to ovens that have been built-in can prove to be the hardest job. Many ovens now have plug-in elements, but others require removal of panels to gain access to fixing screws, nuts and push-on connections. Care must be exercised when removing the panels and insulation materials. As always, ensure that the appliance is isolated. With

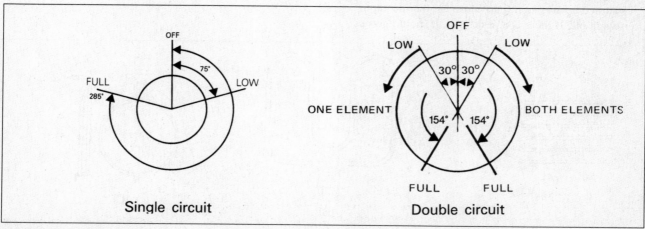

Single and double circuit regulators.

HOB AND OVEN
WATCH POINTS

1	**Make sure the correct replacement only is obtained and fitted.**
2	**Match up all numbers** - model number of appliance, number on switch, etc.
3	**Do not remove any wiring** without first marking connection points and positions.
4	**Ensure as always** that the appliance is isolated; switch off, fuse removed or MCB in off position.
5	**Do not attempt adjustment or repair to regulators.** A faulty unit must be renewed.

appliances such as ovens and hobs, the double-pole isolation switch should be switched to the 'off' position and its fuse or MCB at the consumer unit should be removed or switched off as required.

The following five simple tests help diagnose oven thermostat faults.
● Switch on the power to the cooker by means of the mains switch.
● Turn the oven thermostat knob from 'off' to a low dial setting.
● Within about 10 minutes the oven should have warmed up sufficiently to cause the thermostat to switch off. If there is a pilot light, it should go out indicating the thermostat has switched off.
● Open the oven door and allow heat to escape into the kitchen. After a few seconds, the pilot light should come 'on' again, indicating that the thermostat has cut in and is operating correctly.
● Turn the thermostat dial to the 'off' position. The pilot light should then be out and the oven will cool down normally. If the pilot light stays on and the oven remains hot, the thermostat is defective and should be replaced.

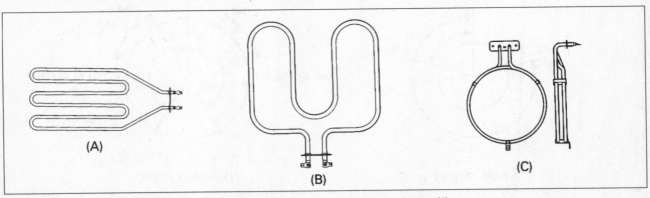

(A)

(B)

(C)

Oven heating element types: conventional oven elements. (A and B) Circular fan oven element (C).

Variable oven thermostat with auxiliary switch (directly behind mounting plate) used for additional switching, such as double oven or fan-assisted variations.

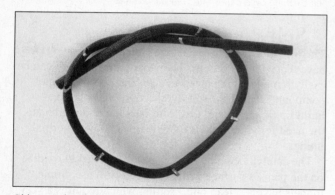

Older type braided oven door seal kit.

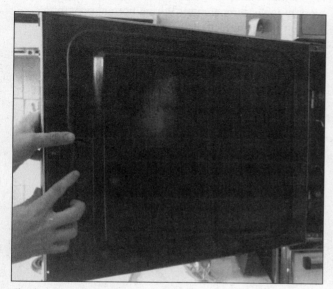

Check door seal position and condition.

Conventional oven faults

Isolate the appliance before removing covers or panels for any reason. All tests for continuity should be carried out with a battery operated test meter only.

● The most likely cause of overheating will be a failure of the thermostat contact points or sealed pressure system. In such a case you will need to fit a new compatible replacement unit.

● Slow initial heating-up times or uneven heat distribution within the oven is usually caused by the failure of one element. Simple testing of the element will highlight the faulty item (see Electrical circuit testing, pages 44-47).

● Failure to heat up at all may be either the thermostat or elements. As elements are the easier of the two to check for continuity, a simple process of elimination will indicate where the fault lies.

● Poor cooking results or undercooking of food can also be caused by a faulty thermostat, which turns off elements at too low a temperature. As mentioned above, the elements are relatively easy to check, so eliminate them first.

Faults in fan ovens

Faults in fan ovens will be similar to those found in conventional ovens. The thermostat and elements can be checked in the same way. As this type of oven has only one element, slow cooking or undercooking is most likely to have been caused by poor air circulation over the element as a result of one of the reasons shown in the chart on page 65.

Non-electrical faults

The main non-electrical fault with ovens, whether free standing or built-in, is the door seal. Seals are made from flexible heat-resistant rubber or woven fibre tubing in many variations of cross-sectional shapes and fixing methods. It is most important that the door be sealed correctly, not only for the efficient operation of the cooker, but also for safety reasons especially in built-in ovens, where the door sides may be close to fitted units.

Door seal kits are available for all of the leading makes and the removal of old seals and the fitting of new ones should not cause any problems. Make sure that you buy the correct replacement and make a note of how the old one is fixed before removing it. If your door seal is held by spring clips, it is advisable to get a kit which includes new springs rather than just the door seal. Make sure the new seal is trimmed to the correct length and all the fixing points are used and secure. Renew seals that become hard, cracked or brittle this will help to keep the

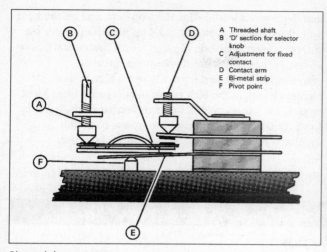

A Threaded shaft
B 'D' section for selector knob
C Adjustment for fixed contact
D Contact arm
E Bi-metal strip
F Pivot point

Bi-metal thermostat.

Steam iron with spray facility.

Descaling

Use a proprietary brand of descaler specially formulated for irons and follow the instructions carefully. Non-toxic, non-caustic, non-corrosive and fully bio-degradable brands are popular. More than one treatment may be necessary if the iron has been used regularly without being descaled. The descaler works by breaking down the bond between the scale and the host surface. The residue is then rinsed away. Before using a descaling product, check the manufacturer's instructions carefully; some self-cleaning irons should not be descaled in this way

even though they will still tend to scale-up when used regularly in very hard water areas.

Electrical problems

The commonest fault is deterioration of the flex caused by its constant movement during use. This may result in a broken inner conductor, giving rise to a plain open circuit fault, or more commonly, an overheating fault due to the movement of the flex causing a make-break action. Heat is generated at this point and will eventually lead to a short circuit within the cable or exposure of the inner wires. This problem occurs more often at the entry point

A variety of descaling products are made for different purposes. Make sure you buy the right type.

of the cable sleeve on the iron. It is essential that the flex is checked regularly for signs of wear or damage. At the first sign of damage renew the whole flex with non-kink iron flex (see Cables, pages 22-25). This problem has been alleviated by better designs, such as the inclusion on some models of a storage facility for the mains lead and easier adaptability for use with either left or right hand.

The introduction of the cordless iron solves the flex problem, although the base unit still requires a mains-powered lead. When the iron is placed on the base unit, it receives power that heats up the sole plate to the correct temperature (via the iron's own thermostat). Sole plates on these irons are thicker than those on conventional irons and normally use a higher wattage element to retain the heat between charge periods. Most models have the same facilities as corded irons, but it is most important to return the iron to the base unit regularly, especially if the steam setting is in use.

Fault finder

Symptom: Will not work at all

POSSIBLE CAUSES	ACTION
Faulty plug or socket.	See Plugs and sockets (pages 12-21).
Fault in flex.	See Cables (pages 22-25) and Electrical circuit testing (pages 44-47). Renew as required.
Open circuit thermostat.	Check that the correct setting is being used. Check the thermostat. See Temperature control devices (pages 40-43) and Electrical circuit testing (pages 44-47).
Open circuit TOC or overheat protective device.	Check for continuity. See Temperature control devices (pages 40-43) and Electrical circuit testing (pages 44-47).
Open circuit element.	See Heating elements (pages 36-39) and Electrical circuit testing (pages 44-47). Ascertain if the element is separate from the sole plate.

Symptom: Iron overheats

POSSIBLE CAUSES	ACTION
Faulty thermostat. Contacts stuck or bi-metal plate failed.	See Temperature control devices (pages 40-43) and Electrical circuit testing (pages 44-47). Renew as required if a pre-set stat is obtainable. If not, you will require a professional repair.
Broken selector knob.	This will give incorrect setting, that is, low indicated on knob, high selected by stat. Look closely for cracks on 'D' shaft of knob. Renew as required.

Symptom: Poor spray/no spray

POSSIBLE CAUSES	ACTION
Tank empty.	Refill and try again. Priming may be required for the pump to function. This varies between makes and models. See the manufacturer's instructions.
Jet/spray nozzle blocked (often called an atomizer).	Most nozzles can be easily removed for cleaning. Some contain filters that require cleaning. See the manufacturer's instructions.

Symptom: No steam (steam iron only)

POSSIBLE CAUSES	ACTION
Incorrect setting of iron.	If the setting is too low, steam cannot be produced. Check that steam setting has been selected.
Water tank empty.	Refill and test, as above.
Water control valve faulty, blocked or scaled.	Test by repeated operation of button or arm, depending on the model. Some allow stripdown of this part, but the iron must have cooled down first and have been isolated. Renewal may be required.
Scale in chamber or steam vents.	Descale. May require more than one treatment if descaling has not been carried out regularly.

IRON
WATCHPOINTS

1 **Regularly check the mains flex** and renew at the first sign of deterioration. Closely inspect the grommet at the iron end of the flex.

2 **Use a flex holder** to alleviate flex wear during use.

3 **Descale regularly** if using tap water.

4 **Do not let the iron cool down** if you accidentally melt a synthetic material on the sole plate or the residue will set.

5 **Use special sole plate cleaner**, available in stick form, to remove starch and fabric conditioner marks.

6 **Avoid damaging the sole plate** by running over sharp objects, such as zips, metal buttons and rivets on jeans.

7 **Iron low-temperature fabrics first** and work up to higher temperatures.

8 **Never leave an unattended iron switched on.**

9 **Always unplug a steam iron when filling** or emptying its water tank.

Fitting a new iron flex

This iron will not work at all. After isolating the appliance the plug was checked with a test meter and found to be sound. This suggests a possible fault in the flex. A new plug will be required if the appliance previously had a moulded plug (see Plugs and sockets, pages 12-19), so bear this in mind when purchasing spare parts.

TOOLS AND MATERIALS

- ☐ Test meter
- ☐ Screwdriver(s)
- ☐ Insulation tape
- ☐ Non-kink iron flex
- ☐ Detergents/soap
- ☐ Plug

1 Isolate the iron and remove the rear cover.

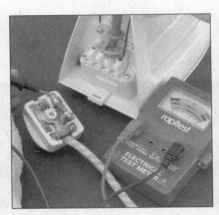

2 Test the three conductor wires for continuity. In this case an open circuit was found on one wire so replacement is necessary.

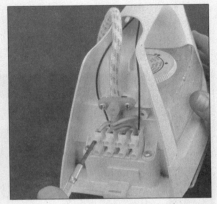

3 Make a note of the position of the wiring and covers before removing the damaged flex. Buy a matching length of non-kink iron flex.

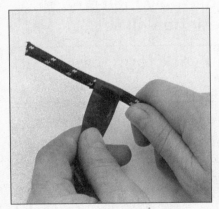

4 Before removing the outer braiding, wrap a strip of insulation tape around the outer of the flex just below the trim point. This prevents the outer cotton braid fraying. Alternatively, if the original flex had a rubber collar, roll this down in place of the tape.

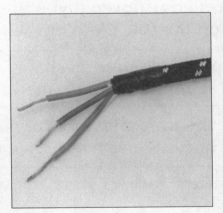

5 Remove the outer braid and inner sheath to expose the three inner wires, taking care not to damage their insulation. If you do, cut back and start again. Remove the insulation from the ends of the conductor wires and securely twist together the strands of each conductor. (You may need to trim to length to match the original.)

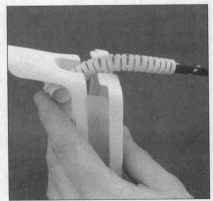

6 Apply a little detergent or soft soap to the grommet to allow the cable to pass easily through.

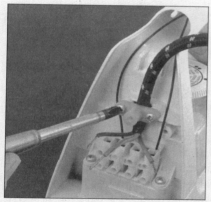

7 Secure the flex by the cord grip within the appliance, ensuring that it is gripped firmly on the outer sheath only.

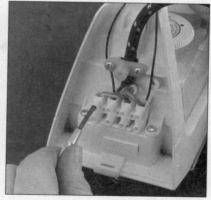

8 Fit the conductor wires to their respective positions, ensuring that any sleeving or protection originally used is fitted to the new flex and that each fitting is secure with no protruding strands.

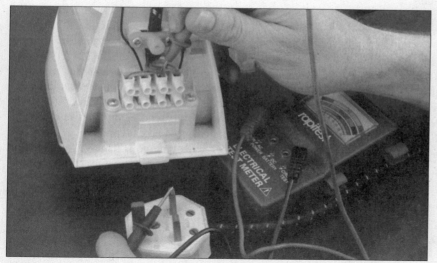

9 Double-check all fixings, covers and connections. Check the continuity of each conductor before refitting the cover.

With covers refitted and secured, a functional test can be carried out
   Ensure the socket is part of a circuit protected by an RCD. If not, a portable RCD should be used (see Safety guide, pages 2-4 and Electrical basics, pages 6-11).

Toasters

The toaster is another appliance that uses heating elements and, in most instances, a bi-metal strip thermostat to control the length of time the bread is exposed to them. This, in turn, relates to the degree of browning required by varying the position of the bi-metal contact points. When bread is inserted, a latched spring system is actuated to hold the bread carrier in place. At the same time, it makes a switch contact to supply power to the elements. The heat from the elements toasts the bread and also heats the bi-metal strip, causing it to bend. The bending of the bi-metal strip either trips the latch system directly or actuates an electrical contact, depending on the type of toaster. An electrical control usually involves the use of a coil which, when energized, creates a magnetic attraction to a movable plate. When attracted to the now magnetized coil, the plate trips the latching device which ejects the bread and simultaneously switches off the elements. Various methods of damping are used to smooth and control the eject operation.

Calibration between bi-metal movement and the toast indicator is required. The way in which this is done differs from make to make, and adjustment should not be carried out unless all other checks prove satisfactory. As always, any cleaning, adjustment or repair must be carried out only on totally isolated appliances, with the switch off and the plug out of the socket.

Common problems

One of the commonest causes of personal injury or damage to equipment is foolishly trying to clear a jammed latch mechanism while the toaster is still plugged in. It is not unusual for the mechanism to jam because debris or a piece of large or curling bread is wedged in. You should never attempt to clear this while the toaster is still plugged in. Moreover, the toaster should never be poked and prodded with knives or any other implements even when it is unplugged.

Toasters use an exposed heating element wound on to an insulating heat-resistant material. Very early toasters used asbestos, but that has long since been safely replaced by more suitable and inert materials. Faults with element windings are not uncommon but single elements for many modern toasters are unobtainable; only complete carriage units of latch mechanism and sets of elements are available from the manufacturers. These may be very expensive in relation to the price of a new toaster.

Some makes still offer individual parts replacement, so enquire first about their availability before discarding your toaster (or before buying it!). With careful use and regular cleaning, you can extend the useful life of all appliances and the toaster is no exception.

The main problem encountered is damage to the mains lead through poor storage, such as wrapping it around the toaster when it is still cooling down after use, or allowing the lead to trail across cookers or hobs. Simple care and attention will prevent most problems. A fault-finding list follows.

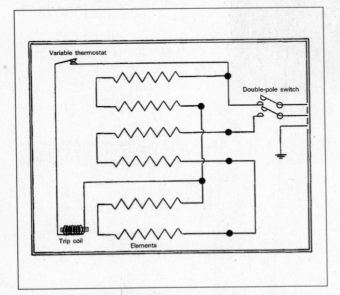

This theoretical diagram shows elements in typical series connection. The live supply to the trip coil is via a tap on the heater circuit. It uses the first four elements as resistors to drop the voltage to the coil.

Fault finder

Symptom: Will not work at all

POSSIBLE CAUSE	ACTION
Faulty socket or plug.	See Plugs and sockets (pages 12-21).
Faulty mains lead.	See Cables (pages 22-25) and Electrical circuit testing (pages 44-47).
Internal loose connections.	Check for continuity; see Electrical circuit testing (pages 44-47).
Failure of switch on latching mechanism (often double-poled).	Check switch contacts for continuity; see Electrical circuit testing (pages 44-47). Also check that the mechanism actuates the switch. Adjust or renew as required.
Latch failing to hold – mechanism or switch.	Check that the latch points engage correctly and hold the bread carriage in the locked position and that the switch is actuated.
One or more elements open circuit. Some toasters have heaters in series, so one open circuit would stop power reaching the others.	Test for continuity; see Electrical circuit testing (pages 44-47). Some models have individual elements as spares.

Symptom: Burns toast on any setting

POSSIBLE CAUSE	ACTION
Bread carriage or latch mechanism sticking.	Clean and check carriage and delatch action, then retest.
Failure of bi-metal strip/stat.	Ascertain whether NC or NO or mechanical stat operation and test as required depending on the type of toaster. See Electrical circuit testing (pages 44-47), or manually check tripping action. Renew if adjustment fails.
Open circuit delatching coil.	Check for continuity; see Electrical circuit testing (pages 44-47). Renew if open circuit.
Contact failure in latch switch, that is shorted together.	Check switch for correct operation (make and break); see Electrical circuit testing (pages 44-47). Renew if found to be faulty.
One element open circuit (if it is the one that heats the bi-metal, excessive trip times will occur).	Check continuity; see Electrical circuit testing (pages 44-47). Renew as required.

Symptom: Toast too light

POSSIBLE CAUSE	ACTION
Latch mechanism nuisance - tripping, that is, failing to hold the bread carriage down.	Check for secure latching or worn latch edges. Renew if worn, otherwise adjust if possible.
Bi-metal strip or stat out of adjustment in relation to indicator.	Adjust bi-metal strip/stat if all other checks are all right.
Some appliances cannot repeat cycles.	Do not adjust the bi-metal strip; this is not a fault but a design weakness on some toasters. Once the toaster is hot, bread toasted subsequently will become increasingly lighter, as the bi-metal strip/stat is already warm. Leave the toaster to cool before inserting more bread or reset the indicator higher to compensate.

Typical toaster repair

Fully isolate the toaster and remove the outer casing. Continuity testing will identify cable, switch or element faults easily, with the appliance isolated.

TOOLS AND MATERIALS

- ☐ Test meter
- ☐ Screwdriver
- ☐ Soft brush
- ☐ Oil

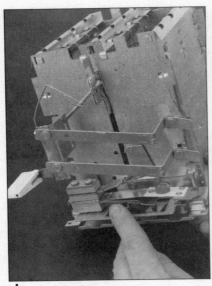

1 Inspect the thermostat.

2 The double-pole switch can be clearly seen. Check the action by latching and delatching manually.

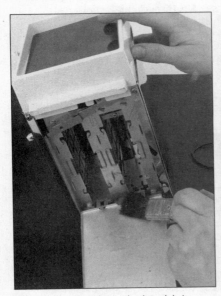

3 Remove crumbs and other debris regularly.

4 Some latch mechanisms may require a little lubrication to avoid sticking. This must be done sparingly and only to the moving parts of the slides. Do not use sprays.

Individual elements, like the ones shown, can be obtained for some makes, but many are complete inner units.

TOASTER
WATCH POINTS

1 **Never attempt to clear a jammed latch mechanism with the toaster still plugged in.**

2 **Never poke any sharp, metal implements into the toaster** – even when unplugged.

3 **Read the manufacturer's instructions** for toasting a single slice of bread.

4 **Do not store the flex wrapped around the toaster,** especially when it is still warm.

5 **Do not position the toaster with the flex trailing across hobs** or cupboard doors.

6 **Do not try to force in slices of bread** that are too thick.

7 **Do not use the toaster for making toasted sandwiches.**

8 **Remove crumbs** and other debris regularly.

Gear drive on hand-held mixer.

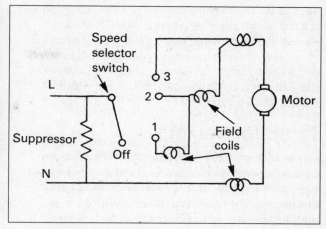

Typical pre-set speed control circuit.

note the meshing positions before removal. Often an aligning mark is moulded on to each gear and it is absolutely imperative that these marks are matched for correct meshing of attachments, such as beaters and dough hooks. When renewing or servicing the gear assembly, lubricate only the worm shaft and gear spacers. Do not overgrease and take care that the grease does not come into contact with any motor parts.

As with any service or repair, ensure that all parts, wiring, screws and covers are refitted in their original positions. Verify the correct earth path if required or check if double-insulated.

Pre-set speed control

This allows the user to select a pre-set speed. Three speeds are usually available on hand-held mixers via a selector switch: 1, 2 and 3 or low, medium and high. Each corresponds to a set motor speed, in turn directly proportional to the beater speed via the drive gear. The switch position selects the size of field coil to be used.

The field coil is wound in such a way that it can be split into three (this is called field tapping). The first position requires power to flow through all three windings, resulting in low speed, but high torque. The second position allows power to flow through two windings, resulting in medium speed and medium torque. The third position selects just the single field winding which results in high speed but low torque.

Continuity testing (see Electrical circuit testing, pages 42-45) assists in fault finding, although failure of one coil will mean complete field coil replacement, if available. Otherwise, a complete replacement of the motor is required. Trace selector switch faults in the same way.

Variable speed control

Unlike the pre-set speed control, variable control allows a greater variation in motor speeds. The motor is a plain AC series-wound brush motor and consequently it is incapable of any variation in speed on its own.

Speed is governed by a separate speed control unit. This unit consists of a printed circuit board with a number of solid-state components, often called the speed module or motor control module. In simple terms, this device interrupts the power supply to the motor at regular intervals. In effect, it pulses the motor. If the pulsing is increased, the motor will run faster and if pulsing is slowed, the motor will run slower.

Pulsing is carried out many times per second by a thyristor or triac. This, in turn, is controlled by other components, one being a variable resistor connected to the speed control knob or slide. When the control is set to the required speed, the resistance allows the thyristor to pulse the motor at a given rate resulting in the required speed.

Such pulsing would create uneven running of the brush motor, so a technique of smoothing is carried out by the module. When the motor is without power during the pulse cycle it will still be rotating. The rotation of the brush motor creates a voltage, the motor being now, in effect, a generator (such voltage is called back-EMF – electro-motive force). The back-EMF produced is used by the module through a diode to smooth the pulses. The utilization of the back-EMF also helps keep the speed of the motor constant even under load. All this occurs many times a second and is undetectable during normal operation. Modules are not repairable and are normally only available as a complete replacement unit.

If speed problems occur, look for burnt components or loose connections. Check all other parts before suspecting or changing the module. The motor should be checked for any shorting insulation, loose wires and worn or damaged brushes (see Motors, pages 26-31 and Electrical circuit testing, pages 42-45). Only when all other possible faults have been eliminated should the module be replaced. Ensure the correct replacement is obtained and note all wires and connections before carrying out a repair.

Table-top mixers

This is a far more robust appliance capable of more continuous use than the hand-held mixer. It has a much larger motor to cope with a wider range of tasks and attachments. The motor can drive high-speed attachments, such as liquidizers, directly by a power take-off point on the armature shaft. The motor also drives a large gearbox via a toothed belt (on early mixers a dog clutch was used to disengage the gearbox when direct motor take-off was in use).

The gearbox forms the top arm of the mixer and has three power take-off points designed to take different attachments. The lower drive is a planet gear drive and is used for mixing, beating, whisking and making dough. The front take-off is a slow-speed drive used for mincing, slicing and shredding. The top gearbox drive is a medium-speed outlet for use with a juice extractor. The attachments mentioned are only a few from the wide selection available for this type of mixer. The speed of each power and take-off point can be varied by altering the drive motor speed.

The motor is a series-wound AC brush motor and all parts are available separately or as a factory assembled

service replacement. It is essential to supply all available information when you are buying or ordering parts, that is, model number, serial number and date of purchase. Manufacturers are constantly upgrading components and failure to give full information may lead to incompatible and, therefore, unusable parts being supplied.

As a result of the high speed of the motor and the long periods that the mixer is in use, motor brush wear and belt wear are the commonest causes of failure. When inspecting motor brushes, remember to mark the existing brushes to ensure that they can be refitted the correct way round. They will have a leading and a trailing edge as the motor rotates in only one direction.

Gearbox problems

These are not very common because this assembly is robustly constructed. A common problem with older mixers is the failure of the dog clutch assembly which transfers drive from the external pulley driven by the belt to gears within the gearbox housing. Several faults can occur.

● Failure of the dog clutch to engage, that is, it cannot be pressed down far enough by the actuating pin situated on the cover. This is caused by wear of the pin. Renewal of cover and pin is usually all that is required.

● Threads within the aluminium top of the dog clutch strip off and no drive is transferred to the shaft. Renew dog on shaft.

● Internal gear at the other end of the drive shaft to the dog clutch splits. This allows all external parts to

Table-top mixer with variable speed control.

The larger gear box unit of the table-top mixer. Note the damage to crown wheel (centre of large gear) on this degreased gear box.

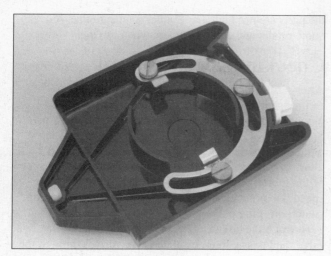

Top cover with dog clutch actuating pin.

Wear on dog clutch threads is common.

Internal drive gear from clutch prone to splitting.

function correctly and the shaft to turn, but fails to transfer drive to the other gears. This requires a new drive pinion. Remove the dog clutch and the top of the gearbox, remembering to note the position of all items during the stripdown. Take care not to cross thread bolts or screws in the soft aluminium casing. The joint of the top and bottom halves of the gearbox can be sealed with a smear of silastic or silastoseal (on early models, red Hermetite was used).

All parts of the gearbox are available separately or as a complete unit. When inspecting or servicing make sure that all the gears mesh correctly and that no teeth are damaged or missing. Renew any suspect items. Before regreasing during a service or repair, first clean thoroughly with paraffin and allow to dry.

After checking that all shims and gears are correctly positioned and the gears mesh, fix the cover on the gearbox using the silastic or silastoseal.

There is a large screw with a fibre washer on the underside of the gearbox. Remove this screw and through the hole insert 135g (4¾oz) of Shell LGP1 with a grease gun. Refit the screw and washer, reassemble the rest of the appliance and refit all covers. Double-check all the work carried out and run the mixer to distribute the grease within the gearbox. Some grease may escape from the top drive outlet; this is normal as it acts as an overflow for any excess grease within the gearbox.

All these checks and tests, except functional testing to verify correct or incorrect operation, should be carried out with the appliance isolated: switch off, plug out. When carrying out a functional test, make sure all cables and wiring have been fitted back into their correct positions. Any parts renewed must be identical to the original specification. Quote model and serial numbers when obtaining spare parts.

Variable speed control on table-top mixers

The speed control on this type of mixer results from the interaction of mechanical action and electronic control. Two variations of electrical control can be found but each uses the same mechanical action.

Two small spring steel plates are fixed to the cooling fan on the lower end of the armature shaft. They are slightly bowed and joined at either end by a small weight. Only the top plate is secured to the fan and shaft. When the motor rotates, the weights on each end of the joined plates are forced outwards by centrifugal force. As they are formed in a bowed configuration and joined at either end, the outward movement of the weights causes the lower plate to be forced downwards. The degree of movement is proportional to the rotational speed of the armature. This movement is used to actuate a switch on the speed control panel.

There are two types of electrical motor control. The first, used on early machines, simply uses the movement of the governor (the centrifugal device described above) to actuate a switch. The switch is mounted on a movable plate beneath the armature and governor. It is usually closed, thus allowing the motor to receive full power. As the speed of the motor increases, the governor distorts and actuates the switch which, in turn, open circuits the direct supply to the motor. Supply is now via a large resistor which slows the motor. As the motor slows, the governor reacts, the switch resets and the motor speeds up. This is a continuous process as long as power continues to be supplied to the motor.

Unmodified, the motor would run at only one speed. Variation in speed is achieved by moving the speed control plate containing the switch further away from the governor. The motor then needs to run faster to create sufficient centrifugal force to activate the switch and the resistor. A greater speed is, therefore, maintained during cycling of the governor and switch. The distance between the governor and the speed control plate is increased or decreased by a cam linked directly to the speed indicator knob. An on/off switch is also included on the speed control plate and operates at the zero position. Later models may also include a manually resettable overload switch. Look for a button on the motor cover base with the head of the mixer raised.

Speed control on later mixers uses a similar governor and switch system, but the simple, large resistor has been replaced by an electronic control which uses a smaller resistor and triac control similar to that described above under Hand-mixers. Although similar in some respects, the parts are not interchangeable, so ensure that you quote model and serial numbers when buying.

Checking speed control

After service or repair, the calibration of the speed control should be checked. The speed control plate is mounted on two spring-loaded screws that act as a pivot. Speed control is adjusted by turning these screws in or out. It is important to adjust the screws evenly, only half a turn at a time. Clockwise (tightening) reduces the speed of the motor; anticlockwise (slackening) increases the speed. Do not adjust the screws with the mixer running: switch off, plug out.

To reach the adjusting screw, raise the head of the mixer and pass a long, insulated screwdriver through the hole in the base cover of the motor. The only tools required are the screwdriver and a stop watch or watch with a second hand or read-out.

● Ensure all parts and covers are fitted to the machine correctly. Do not fit any attachments to the mixer for the test.
● Raise the head of the mixer and leave it in this position.
● Run the mixer at full speed (the maximum setting on the dial) for at least three minutes to warm up.
● Turn the speed control knob to the minimum setting.
● With the mixer running on minimum, count the rotations of the planet hub drive. Do this within 15 seconds of turning from maximum to minimum setting to obtain a correct reading. Use the stop watch to count rotations for exactly one minute. The correct setting is between 60 and 68 revolutions per minute of the planet hub.

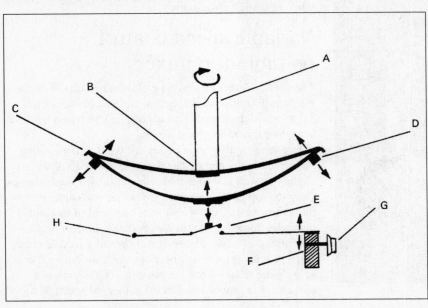

Motor mechanical speed control.
A Armature shaft
B Fixing point to shaft (normally part of cooling fan)
C Spring steel plates
D Weights
E Normally 'open' switch
F Cam to vary position of switch 'E' by moving mounting plate
G Speed selector knob
H Pivot point of mounting p late (adjustable for speed calibration)

- If you count more or fewer rotations per minute, switch off and unplug. Adjust as required: clockwise to reduce speed and anticlockwise to increase speed. Remember, adjust both screws evenly and only one half turn at a time.
- Remove your screwdriver. Plug in and switch on. If less than 15 seconds have elapsed since the last test, run on minimum and repeat the rotations count. If more than 15 seconds have passed, run again at maximum for three minutes and then reduce to minimum for the count.
- Repeat until the correct setting is achieved. If difficulty is encountered in setting the speed, repeat the whole test procedure.

Belt tension adjustment

The most recent table-top mixers have adjustable drive belts. To maintain optimum efficiency and to avoid excessive wear, the belt tension should be checked as shown. Adjust by loosening the three motor mounting bolts and turning the small adjusting bush to the rear of the mixer, thus allowing the motor to slide as required to achieve the optimum tension. Ensure all bolts are tightened and re-check tension. Squeeze the belt with thumb and forefinger at point A. If the tension is correct, the top and bottom of the belt should be parallel between B and C. Adjust the belt as required.

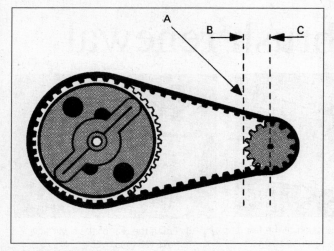

Adjusting belt tension

Repairing a hand-held mixer

TOOLS AND MATERIALS
- ☐ Test maker
- ☐ Screwdriver
- ☐ Molykote grease
- ☐ Motor brushes

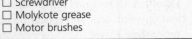

1 This mixer works only on medium or high speeds. Although power is obviously getting to the appliance, both plug and cable should be thoroughly checked as a matter of course.

2 Identify the fixing screws or clips that need to be removed for access to the interior. Make a note of all fixing points and positions before removing them from the isolated mixer.

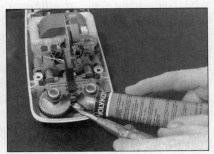

3 Test for continuity using the leap-frog method (see pages 43-45).

4 A simple open circuit fault in the low speed circuit indicates a broken wire, which is easily replaced. If the fault had been in the field coil a replacement motor would have been required.

5 Make a thorough check of all other parts. Lubricating the drive point of worm and gears with a little Molykote grease is a worthwhile maintenance procedure.

Double-check all parts before refitting the casing. Moving the selector switch to the middle setting may make locating the casing much easier. Carefully fit all the fixing screws back in their original places. Fully assembled, the mixer is ready for a functional test.

Table-top mixer brush renewal

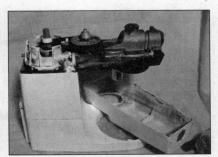

1 This mixer runs unevenly and testing has shown the motor brushes to be suspect.

2 Note the correct position of the fixing plate. Remove the securing screws.

3 By lifting the rear of the cover first, remove the top cover.

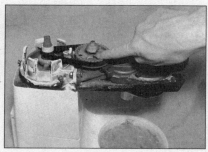

4 Ease off the belt by moving it up off the large pulley.

5 Slacken off the motor centralizing screw just a little.

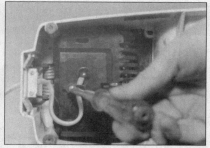

6 Remove the terminal cover at the base of the machine, noting the connections first.

7 Unscrew the four screws and remove the motor cover to allow access to the two screws holding the latch bar system.

8 With the cover removed and terminal board allowed to drop into the motor area, loosen the four motor fixing screws.

9 When all four screws are free, you can manoeuvre out the unit. It is essential that the small washers are refitted to both sides of the rubber motor mounts.

10 Remove the motor, unscrew the brushes and renew both if either is shorter than 5mm (1/5 inch). Check the commutator; if it shows no damage fit a new motor brush.

Refitting is a careful reversal of the stripdown procedure, ensuring that all parts and cables are replaced as they were originally. It is essential that the motor be central upon completion. A special tool may be used for this purpose but if this is not available, use the top securing/adjusting screws to centralize the small drive shaft of the motor in relation to the chrome fixing plate. When central, use the locking nuts to secure their positions.

Double-check the position when the top cover is refitted with the fixing plate. Carry out a functional test on an RCD protected circuit and check the speed as detailed above.

Chapter 4

Living room appliances

Portable heaters

Three main types of domestic, free-standing, portable electric heaters are widely used: radiant, convector and fan heaters. Some appliances combine different heater types, such as a convector plus a radiant bar.

Radiant heaters

Heat is produced by an element that glows red-hot when power is supplied to it. The heat generated by this action is directed by a highly polished reflector through an open front protected by a metal grill. The element can be externally wound on a ceramic mount or internally mounted in a heat-resistant silica glass tube. Simple switching of the element/s is included and faults can easily be traced. See Electrical circuit testing (pages 44-48), for continuity testing of the elements.

Convector heaters

Heating in these is by an open spiral/spring element supported on mica or ceramic plates at the base of the unit. No moving parts are used to distribute heat; only normal convection air current created by warm air rising from the heater.

A simple on/off switch is usually included and often a variable thermostat of the bi-metal type is used to maintain a pre-set temperature by switching the element on or off as required. A TOC is often fitted to prevent overheating. Circuit testing can be carried out to ascertain faults; see Electrical circuit testing (pages 44-48) and Temperature control devices (pages 40-43).

Fan heaters

The fan heater is the most popular of all portable heaters, mainly because of its compact size and its ability to heat a large room quickly. This is done in a similar way to the hairdryer, but a much larger element is used (up to 3kW).

It may have a variable heat output – typically 700W, 1300W and 3,000W – by means of a switchable combination of elements and some have thermostats. A cold blow facility is often included for summer use; this simply allows the motor and fan to run without any of the elements in circuit.

A shaded-pole motor is normally used. Large fans or barrel fans are attached directly to the rotor to blow air over the element assembly. This creates a powerful airflow that rapidly heats (or helps cool) the room.

Problems

All three types of heaters must have the correct rated cable fitted and care should be taken, not only in repair and servicing, but in the safe use and positioning of all heating appliances.

The fan heater is more complex than the other two types of heater and may have mechanical as well as electrical problems. A safety thermostat/TOC is incorporated to switch off the element should motor failure occur.

Most heaters require three-core earthed flex, but some modern fan heaters may be double insulated and have only two-core flex fitted. Ensure the correct cable is fitted when renewing and check the rating plate to verify if the appliance is double insulated (see Safety guide, pages 2-4).

It is essential that all wiring and covers are refitted in their correct positions after servicing or repair. Make a note of each item and its position during stripdown.

Both convector and radiant appliances require little maintenance. Periodically, check the mains lead for damage or wear and tear along its whole length. Inspect cable sleeves and terminal block connections, making sure they are tight and no overheating is present. Regularly check the air inlet grilles on the base of a convector heater for fluff and debris and clean as necessary.

Keep the reflector on radiant heaters clean and bright, but take care when cleaning not to damage the ceramic or glass mounts of the elements. Check the radiant bar ends, making sure they are tight and a good electrical connection is being made. When cleaning or inspecting these appliances, ensure a correct earth path exists between all linked metal parts and the earth pin of the plug, unless it is a double insulated appliance.

Radiant heater.

Fan heater.

Convector heater.

Fault finder

Symptom: Will not work at all

POSSIBLE CAUSE	ACTION
Faulty mains lead or plug/socket.	See Plugs and sockets (pages 12-21), Cables (pages 22-25) and Electrical circuit testing (pages 44-47).
Variable thermostat (if fitted) incorrectly set or faulty.	Check variable thermostat for correct setting and continuity. See Temperature control devices (pages 40-43) and Electrical circuit testing (pages 44-47). Do not adjust. Faulty thermostats need to be replaced.
TOC tripped or failed. (Some appliances may have self-resetting TOCs, others manual reset.)	Check for continuity; see Electrical circuit testing (pages 44-47). Check for blockage of fan/motor seizure. Reset TOC if applicable and retest. Renew auto reset TOC if suspect.
Internal wiring fault.	Check all connections. Tighten or renew if suspect. See Electrical circuit testing (pages 44-47).
Switch failure.	Check switch action (audible clicks) and verify continuity. Inspect closely for overheating and renew if suspect. Models with multi-select switch banks require renewal of complete switch unit even if only one switch has failed.

Symptom: Motor runs but no heat produced

POSSIBLE CAUSE	ACTION
TOC tripped or failed. (Some appliances may have self-resetting, others manual reset TOCs)	Check for continuity; see Electrical circuit testing (pages 44-47). Check for blockage or fan/motor seizure. Reset TOC if applicable and retest. Renew auto reset TOC if suspect.
Open circuit heater.	Check continuity of heater element; see Electrical circuit testing (pages 44-47).
Internal wiring fault.	Check all connections, tighten or renew if suspect. See Electrical circuit testing (pages 44-47).
Switch failure.	Check switch action (audible clicks) and verify continuity. Inspect closely for overheating and renew if suspect. Models with multi-select switch banks usually require a complete renewal even if only one switch has failed.

All the faults listed under this symptom can cause damage to the heater TOC by tripping on and off as heating and cooling takes place because no air is flowing over the elements. TOC renewal may be required if cycling has happened over a long period of time. Failure to do so may cause nuisance-tripping after the original fault has been rectified. This is because the TOC has weakened and trips at a lower temperature than normal. This type of fault is often called temperamental TOC.

Symptom: Element heats but no motor action	
POSSIBLE CAUSE	**ACTION**
Open circuit motor.	Check continuity; see Electrical circuit testing (pages 44-47). Failure of coil or internal TOC will require renewal of motor.
Fan or motor jammed.	Check all moving parts and bearings. Clean or renew as required.
Switch failure.	Check switch action (audible clicks) and verify continuity. Inspect closely for overheating and renew if suspect. Models with multi-select switch banks usually require complete renewal of switch unit even if only one switch has failed.

Symptom: Noisy	
POSSIBLE CAUSE	**ACTION**
Debris on fan assembly.	Clean fan and inlet grilles and check for free rotation.
Damaged or bent fan.	This is often caused by misuse or accidental dropping of appliance. Check for free rotation of fan. Check housing position.
Bearing fault on motor or fan. This fault will cause slow running and subsequently reduced air flow. See TOC note under above symptom.	Check for excessive movement on bearings. On motor, check closely that rotor does not foul the stator because of worn bearings. This causes the rotor to be pulled on to the stator only when power creates the powerful magnetic field.

All the above checks and tests, except functional testing to verify correct or incorrect operation, must be carried out with the appliance isolated: switch off, plug out. When carrying out a functional test, take care to avoid parts of the appliance that remain hot.

PORTABLE HEATERS
WATCHPOINTS

1 **Ensure all air grilles and inlets are free from fluff.**

2 **Apply a drop of light machine oil** every six months to extend the life of the motor and fan bearings.

3 **Make sure bladed fans, if removed, are refitted in the correct position,** as they are left-handed and right-handed.

4 **Take great care in removal and storage during repair** or servicing, as all fans are easily damaged.

Fan heater repair

This fan heater alternates between heating but with no motor action and operating noisily. Isolate the appliance and note the positions of the fixing screws grilles, etc.

TOOLS AND MATERIALS

☐ Screwdriver/Small soft brush
☐ Light machine oil

1 Remove the two screws securing the front grille.

2 Ease the front grille from its position. Remove the top cover.

3 Removing the cover gives access to the motor and fan unit as well as the heater and TOC.

4 Thoroughly clean the motor, fans and grilles before inspecting more closely.

5 A loose motor securing pin is found during cleaning. This was allowing the motor to shift out of position, causing the fans to catch on the housing. Reposition the motor correctly and tighten the fixing pin. Spin the fans manually to make sure they do not foul the housing.

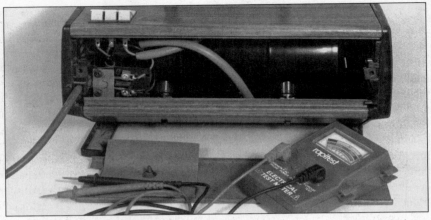

6 Apply a little light machine oil to the motor bearings. Check that all parts are in their original positions before refitting the covers.

7 Remove the rear screws and remove the rear panel to gain access to the terminal block and switch bank for testing and inspection. With all panels refitted and all tests proving all right, the heater is ready for a functional test with an RCD in circuit.

HEATER
W A T C H POINTS

1	**Never use room heaters for drying** or airing clothes.
2	**Do not restrict airflow around heaters** or place them close to other items.
3	**Do not use any heater without its safety guard,** with its covers removed or when damaged.
4	**Do not use an unsuitable extension lead.**
5	**Never use a room heater outdoors.**

Video and audio equipment

Most households have at least one item of video and audio equipment: television, video, sound system, CD player and so on. As a rule, it is not wise for the amateur to attempt to repair such high tech equipment, as this requires expert knowledge, expensive equipment and detailed service manuals. The intricate nature of internal mechanical and electronic components and the high voltages make it inadvisable to remove panels or outer covers. It is more sensible to leave this to the skills of the trained specialist.

However, there is much the user can do to prevent problems occurring and to extend the life of the product and keep it in peak condition. In addition, do not jump to the conclusion that all faults on electronic equipment have complex causes. Poor connections, lack of care and maintenance and misunderstanding the correct way to operate the appliance account for a very large proportion of faults. With a little thought and the correct safe approach, they are also the easiest to overcome – often at little or no cost.

Videos

The number of households with video cassette recorders (VCRs) has increased enormously in recent years. Product reliability has improved along with this increased popularity. This is excellent news for owners but may be bad news for the equipment! More reliability has resulted in fewer visits from the service engineer. As a result, apathy on the part of the owner is common, often proved by the lack of maintenance.

Dirt from the atmosphere, dust from carpets and oxide dust from tape wear build up within and upon the components of the machine. As a result, picture and sound quality will drop but, because this is a gradual process, it tends to be disregarded until the build-up of deposits begins to damage the video tapes. Serious damage to the video head and other parts of the mechanism can also result from lack of cleaning. A very expensive repair requiring several new parts will then be necessary. All this can be avoided quite simply by regular use of a high-quality cleaning system like the one shown here. Frequency depends on how often the video is used.

Thorough cleaning of internal electronic components cannot be achieved with a cassette-based system. It is better carried out by a qualified engineer at a time when internal adjustments or parts renewal is required.

Avoid standing video recorders directly on the carpet beneath the television set. Fluff and dust are more readily drawn in by cooling fans within the unit. The air intake vents on some machines are underneath, in which case they would be completely blocked. Use a proper video stand.

Video cleaning systems

When a video tape is inserted into the video and set to play or record it is drawn into the tape mechanism. A large rotating head scans the tape during record and playback; two static heads are used for erase and audio respectively. The rotating video head is easily damaged. Dirt and oxide shed from the tape are unwelcome at any point along the tape path, but the video head is most at risk from even the smallest particles. If this head becomes scratched, dirt will adhere more readily to it.

Proper use, care and cleaning will prolong the life of your VCR.

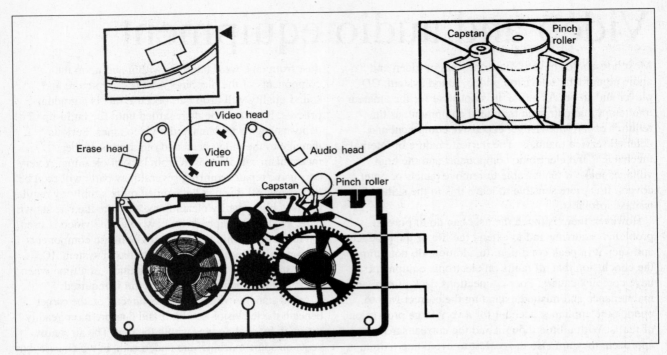

Interior of video cleaning system.

Poor quality tape cleaning systems can add to the problem. A poor dry system may be too abrasive and shed fibres during the cleaning process and a poor wet system may leave a residue of cleaning fluid. Use only a high-quality kit that protects as well as cleans.

The kit illustrated mimics the original tape path and uses a wet system (liquid solvent) that is fibre-free, with pads that also clean the pinch roller. The system is automatic and extremely easy to use. The main cassette can perform 50 cleaning cycles; a fresh section of cleaning tape is used each time. Another good feature is that after the 50 cycles have been used, a refill kit is available for replenishing the cassette with pads, tape and fluid. A further bonus is that the cleaning solution no longer contains Freon, which is a CFC, and the removal of this from the product is most welcome in environmental terms.

Make sure you buy a cleaning system that suits the format of your machine (VHS, BETA, UMATIC, etc.). Follow the manufacturer's instructions and do not be tempted to use more than the specified amount of cleaning fluid per cycle, as an excess could create further problems.

Avoiding problems

Not all problems are a result of dirty video heads, so if there is no improvement after three cleaning cycles, try another tape on playback; perhaps a fault exists on the original tape. If the fault persists, check all connections to and from the video as detailed below. If the fault still remains, then an internal mechanical or electrical fault is likely and this will require the expertise of a video engineer.

When purchasing tapes, select a high-quality named brand. Beware of cheap tapes of dubious origin as these are more likely to break and get trapped in the tape run. They may also shed the oxide coating causing wear of the heads and, if excessive, on the pinch roller too, causing the video to 'eat' a tape.

A sure way to increase the chances of tape or video

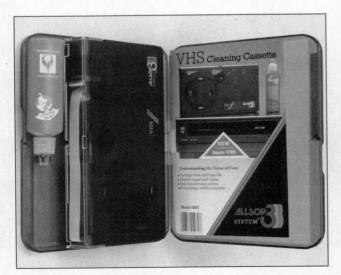

A high-quality video cleaning system.

head wear is to over-use the pause facility. This is due to the tape's being held in one position while the head constantly scans (rotates) across it. Also avoid excessive use of the stop-start control because this can stretch the tape and cause picture quality problems.

Remember, to get the best from your video recorder (or any appliance for that matter) it is an advantage if you fully understand the way in which your particular machine should be used. Take time to read the manufacturer's instruction booklet thoroughly. It is the only way to get the most from your machine and it will help you to understand problems that may occur. Sometimes the apparent problem is nothing more than an obscure but perfectly correct function of the unit.

Tapes

Store tapes vertically to help prevent their stretching or loops forming and always put them in their cases tape face in. Do not store them near magnetic sources, such as loudspeakers or motors. As the signal is recorded on the tape in a magnetic format by the video, other sources of magnetism can distort or blank it. Do not store tapes in direct sunlight or where temperatures may be too high or too low. When hiring tapes from video clubs, check that

the tape and cassette are in good condition. Do not touch the tape because grease from fingers will damage both tape and video head, but inspect the entry points for dust or flaking of the oxide (fine brownish powder or flakes). Other users may not have been as careful as they should or their video recorders may have caused tape damage. One run of a faulty tape can be enough to cause serious head damage for the future. When bringing in a tape from a cold environment, let the cassette acclimatize before playing it. Otherwise condensation may form on the tape which could cause it to stick to the video head. The same also applies to bringing a video machine into a warm room from a cold environment, but a longer period should be allowed. Some machines have condensation protection sensors and will not operate until they are clear.

Some faults can be identified by inspecting the tape itself. Avoid touching the tape surface with the fingers. If blemishes or damage are found, do not use the tape again.

Mechanical problems

The tape mechanism is mechanical as well as electrical. There are several moving parts within the machine which require lubricating occasionally to keep the unit operating correctly. This is best carried out by a qualified

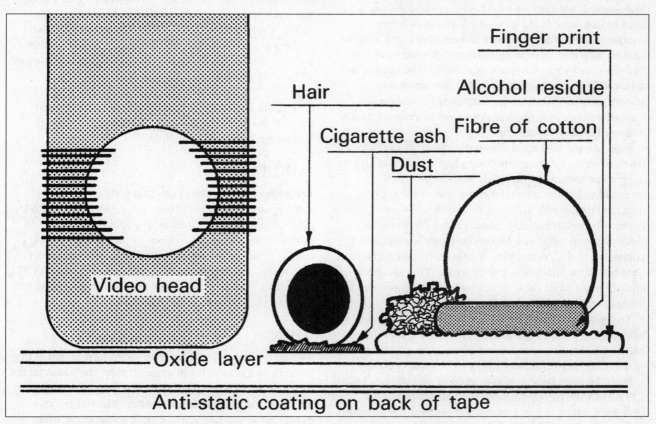

Video head contamination. This diagram illustrates just how closely the video head scans the tape. The particles of debris are to the same scale.

Typical sockets.

technician because only small amounts of lubrication are required on specific areas. Several adjustments may also be required to compensate for deterioration and use. Such settings and types of lubrication differ between makes and models and it is unwise to attempt any such maintenance yourself.

Cables and connectors

Numerous combinations of different connections may be used to link your video to your television or other equipment. What they all have in common is the need to pass an interference-free signal between video and television or video, television and audio. The human ear can readily compensate for interference on an audio system and will often accept surprisingly poor quality, but vision is more acute and even a small drop in quality will not be easily tolerated.

Poor connections are the commonest cable faults as a result of stress on the connecting plug or socket. Dirt on the pins or socket can seriously impair the signal transmitted by the cable. If a connector or socket is damaged or the pins are bent, do not try to force a connection between them. Some cables carry several small wires to multi-pin sockets or plugs which must be connected to the correct pins within the fitting and a high quality secure joint must also be made. This applies equally to co-axial cable which has only an inner and an outer connection.

Ready-made cables are available to fit all situations; be advised to go for a high-quality one, even if it seems expensive. Cutting corners and buying cheap cables and connectors may ultimately prove to be false economy.

With the increasing sophistication of electronics, video, CD and so on, the area behind the various units can become a confusing and messy conglomeration of cables and connectors. You will almost certainly have spent a lot of time setting up the equipment and the resulting mass of (usually black) wires can cause quite a headache when a fault arises. Which wire belongs where? Similarly, if the equipment is moved and a connection dislodged, which one is it? It is far easier to take a little time to keep all wires and connectors tidy.

When adding to your equipment, a little forward planning when installing it will help. Mark each cable with coloured tape or stickers from and to. Use a code that suits you and is easy to remember, such as V for video, A for audio, C for CD, etc. Do not rely on the stickers alone; use a belt-and-braces approach (children and animals delight in removing stickers). Keep a log of all new equipment and how you connected it up originally. Although this approach may take a little extra time at the beginning, it can save hours of work and frustration later on and reduce the chance of damage caused by incorrect connection.

Audio

The audio tape system works in a similar way to the video system described above. However, in an audio tape player the tape is fed in front of a fixed head and information is either laid down or picked up by it. A similar pinch wheel/roller system is used to transport the tape across the head. On units with auto reverse facility, two pinch wheels will be present, on each side of the head, to pull the tape in the direction required.

Tapes

The tape, although smaller than video tape, is much the same in that is uses ferric oxide to store the audio track magnetically. Problems of dust, dirt and oxide shedding are the same as for video recorders. Most of us have experienced the 'eating the tape' phenomenon, often caused by dirt or deposits on the pinch roller/wheel and

Variations of cable connectors commonly used.

VIDEO AND AUDIO EQUIPMENT
WATCH POINTS

1 **Route cables carefully** to avoid stretching and kinking.

2 **Store all cables in coils,** not bent or twisted together.

3 **Store cables out of the reach of children** and pets.

4 **Do not leave cables lying where people or pieces of furniture can stand on them.**

Fault finder (Videos)

Symptom: Tape cut or trapped in mechanism

POSSIBLE CAUSE	ACTION
Excessive dirt or condensation build-up on video head.	If tape cassette can be removed easily, allow moisture to evaporate and use cleaning cassette.
Pinch roller fault.	If this fails or cassette will not eject, do not force it. Consult a technician.

Symptom: Flaking or cracking

POSSIBLE CAUSE	ACTION
Possible poor quality tape.	Check by inspecting your other better quality tapes.
Incorrect tape position in cassette.	Has the cassette been dropped? Check other tapes to see if they are all right. If so, try again; if not, consult a technician.
Incorrect cassette take-up .	Consult a technician.

Symptom: Edge of tape damaged. Herring-bone marks

POSSIBLE CAUSE	ACTION
Pinch roller dirty.	Use cleaning cassette. If fault persists, consult a technician.
Pinch roller tension/position wrong.	Consult a technician.

Symptom: Diagonal scratches on part or all of tape

POSSIBLE CAUSE	ACTION
Condensation on video head.	Allow machine or tape to acclimatize. Retest with a new tape. If no improvement, use the cleaning cassette. If there is still no improvement, consult a technician.
Dirt on video head or damage to head.	Use the cleaning cassette. If this has not been done for some time, more than one run may be required. If no improvement after three runs, consult a technician.

Symptom: Regularly spaced horizontal marks

POSSIBLE CAUSE	ACTION
Dirt or defect on VTR tape guide.	Use the cleaning cassette. If no improvement, consult a technician.

Symptom: Continuous line near edges of tape	
POSSIBLE CAUSE	**ACTION**
Tape carriage mechanism misaligned.	Consult a technician.

Symptom: Continuous line on centre of tape	
POSSIBLE CAUSE	**ACTION**
Dirt or mark on tape guide, tape mechanism or erase/audio head.	Use the cleaning cassette. If the fault persists, consult a technician as there may be damage to the roller.

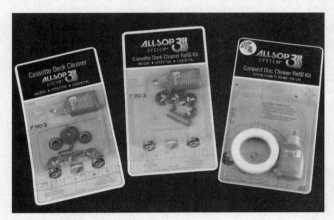

Audio cleaning kit and refills.

Tape trouble is often caused by dirt.

capstan. The sticky deposit makes the tape stick to the pinch roller and is subsequently wrapped around it. It can usually be removed quite easily although it will, of course, be useless. The problem will recur if thorough cleaning is not carried out.

The tape cleaner cassette system shown here works in the same way as the video cleaning system described on page 123. The audio version shown is capable of cleaning both pinch rollers simultaneously on auto reverse systems, as well as cleaning the head.

Tape damage is similar to that described for video tapes. In severe cases, a worn or damaged pinch roller/wheel must be replaced. Damage can be seen by looking into the tape compartment. A new pinch roller/wheel is a dull black colour. Worn or dirty pinch rollers/wheels are rust-coloured (due to the oxide deposits), shiny and sticky. If cleaning does not improve the condition, a new part will be necessary. This is best left to a qualified technician. Remember regular cleaning with a reliable system can prevent this problem.

Compact discs

There are no faults with CD players that are within the capabilities of the DIY repairer. Do not attempt adjustment or servicing to any internal components; leave it to a trained service engineer. However, looking after your equipment properly minimizes the possibility of faults occurring.

The first consideration is the positioning and environment of the player. Do not place a CD unit in strong sunlight, near heat or in damp or humid conditions. The CD system requires very close tolerances to be maintained for accurate disc reading and sound reproduction.

Much is made of the fact that the disc makes no physical contact with the pick-up system. Many have been mistakenly led to believe that this means it can be handled freely and requires little protection or cleaning. Even a fingerprint on the disc can cause the reading light beam to be deflected or to misread, resulting in jumping or skipping of tracks. The skipping is often mistakenly blamed on a fault within the player when, in fact, it is a

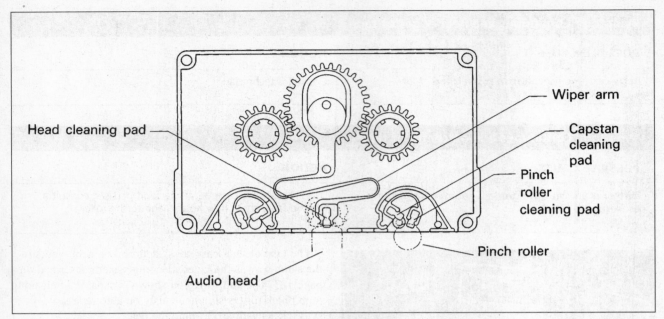

Tape cleaner cassette. Note the two pinch roller cleaning pads for use on auto reverse decks.

user fault. To avoid this problem, respect the disc and use a proper disc cleaner. The one shown uses a radial cleaning action to avoid damaging the surface of the CD.

CD systems can reproduce sounds across an extremely wide range with little or no distortion. As there is no physical contact between the disc and the pick-up, no noise or distortion is added to the signal which is amplified for us to listen to or view. The sound (or vision) is not stored by a series of ridges along a groove like a vinyl record, but in a sequence of pits etched into the flat surface of the disc. These are read by a laser beam that is tuned to detect each pit as it passes. The disc rotates at between 200 and 500 rpm when data is being read. A scratch in a straight line from inner to outer would, therefore, only be seen by the laser for the smallest fraction of a second and could be filtered out by the error correction circuitry incorporated in the

equipment. However, should the scratch or debris, such as a hair, run in line to the laid down track, much more data would be lost and, because this cannot be corrected, audible distortion or skipping would be the inevitable result.

Record decks

Record decks are made up of three main parts: a driven turntable on which the record is placed, a stylus (needle) to follow the contours of the record groove and a drive for the turntable and amplification circuitry to boost the signal picked up from the record by the stylus.

There are numerous variations, ranging from the cheap and simple to extremely complex systems with stroboscopic control of the turntable speed, balance systems for stylus contact weight, and very sophisticated

Tape deck showing pinch roller drive, record head and erase head. On auto reverse decks a second pinch roller is present.

CD cleaning system.

amplification systems. This diversity and complexity of internal components means that DIY repairs and maintenance are generally restricted to the accessible exterior parts of the deck only. Problems with amplification and control circuitry are better left to a qualified technician. Direct your efforts to preventing problems.

However, some decks use belt driven turntables and belt renewal is possible, provided you take care not to damage other items and alter adjustment settings. Isolate the machine before any repairs are made. Even if belt renewal is possible, obtaining the correct size belt replacement may prove difficult. Ensure that the new belt matches the original exactly to avoid any further damage.

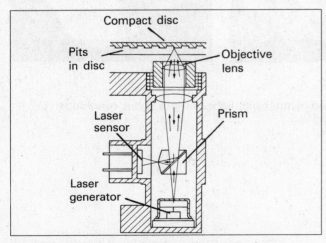

Simplified system of disc reading operation on a CD player.

Avoiding problems

Whether cheap and simple or astronomically expensive, all decks are averse to dirt and debris which is statically attracted to the vinyl record. It then damages the stylus resulting in the all-too-familiar click, pop and jumping of the track.

Sound is stored on a vinyl record on a continuous groove starting at the outer edge and finishing at the centre of the disc. The groove has microscopic ridges proportional in size to the sound wave that created them. When the record rotates, the stylus is deflected by these ridges as it runs in the groove. These minute deflections are then amplified. Two requirements must be met for the stylus to track correctly. The first is that the groove of the record is free from all blemishes and foreign matter to which the stylus would react. The other is that the arm holding the stylus must apply just enough weight to hold the point within the groove (usually 1-2 grams) but not so much as to create excessive wearing of the groove.

The stylus travels as far as 426m (1,400 feet) along the groove during the playing of only one side of a record. The point of the stylus moves extremely quickly as it reacts to the thousands of ridges it continually encounters. All this results in friction which, in turn, creates heat. Surprisingly, the temperature at the tip of the stylus may be as high as 500°C (932°F).

If dirt and grease left on a record come into contact with the hot stylus, a hard crystalline deposit forms on the stylus. This not only reduces the playback quality but

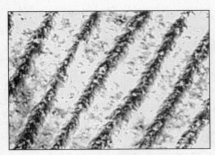

This magnified section of a vinyl record shows severe contamination.

This shows what the surface of a vinyl record should look like.

Use a high-quality cleaning system to maintain both sound and equipment.

also tends to wear away the higher frequency ridges on the record, resulting in permanent damage. Debris within the grooves and surface of the record can include cigarette ash, household dust, chemicals such as tobacco tar, aerosol sprays, mildew and grease and acid from fingerprints. Correct cleaning is therefore essential to maintain sound quality and record life and to reduce the frequency of stylus renewal. Make sure a high-quality cleaner is used.

The stylus

There are over 1,500 different types of stylus in use today, but they all have several things in common. To operate correctly they need to be cleaned regularly and handled with care to avoid damaging the tip. Remember that a build-up of dirt or a damaged stylus will not only give poor sound reproduction when playing a record, but will eventually cause permanent damage to the groove of the record. To prevent this, the stylus should be cleaned at

least once every 20 LPs. A stylus cleaning kit is available which contains cleaning fluid and a specially designed brush. Each kit comes with detailed instructions which must be followed to eliminate the possibility of damage to this delicate piece of equipment.

At some point, whether due to wear or damage, the stylus will need to be replaced. To postpone replacement is a false economy, as permanent damage to your records would be inevitable. You will need to have available all possible information about your player and the type of stylus it uses to ensure that you obtain the correct replacement.

- Ensure you have the brand name of your product.
- Most makes also have a model number.
- Look closely at the old stylus, it should have a unique number.
- Make a note of the colour of the stylus body (this often helps to locate the correct type).

As with any repair, make a note of the correct position

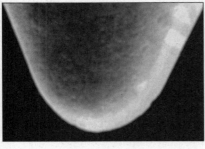

1

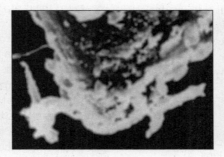

2

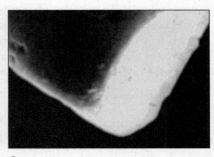

3

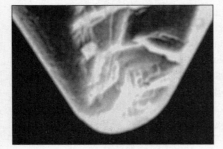

4

A series of magnified pictures highlights various stylus conditions:
1 stylus in good condition
2 contaminated stylus
3 worn stylus
4 damaged stylus.

of the stylus before removal and take care when removing and refitting. Fixings differ greatly from simple clip-in types to those which require a fine watchmaker's screwdriver to remove and refit them. Some may come in a cartridge form which clicks in and out of position. Ensure that connections or contacts are correctly positioned before refitting and do not use excessive force for removal or refitting. Often the angle at which the cartridge is removed and refitted is critical, so take care and avoid rough handling.

Television

This is another appliance with internal functions that are best left to those with the relevant skills and tools, the proper manuals and an in-depth knowledge. Even though it is quite easy to do so, do not be tempted to remove the cover, which would expose parts that are not only easily damaged, but may carry high voltages. Leave all internal faults, service and repair to qualified engineers.

Nevertheless, many things can point to a fault within the appliance which turns out to be something external to it and within the realms of DIY. This does not extend to roof-mounted aerials. Although the fitting and adjustment of aerials is essentially a simple task, the correct equipment for gaining safe access to the roof is essential: a good set of ladders, including roof ladders, combined with a good head for heights. This work is better left to the professional. In areas with good reception, aerials can be mounted in the loft space, pre-empting any problems of damage due to weather conditions, corrosion or poor connections caused by the elements.

Picture problems

Picture problems may result from a poor or weak signal being received by the set. This can happen with both indoor and outdoor aerials. The cause can be as follows.

● Adverse weather conditions (temporary fault).
● An incorrectly tuned set (one channel poor, others all right).
● Poor reception area (house situated in a valley).
● Incorrect aerial direction or a faulty cable or connection.

A simple process of elimination may ascertain if the problem is an external fault or if the set itself has a fault. The remedies are as follows.

● Check with neighbours to see if they are having the same picture problem.
● Check tuning of faulty channel. Refer to the manufacturer's instructions, as tuning differs between makes and models.
● Check with your neighbours. Poor reception will not be intermittent but continual and might be alleviated

by using a signal amplifier like the one shown. As its name implies, the signal is amplified by the unit before the video or television receives it, thus enhancing your picture quality.

● Check aerial direction by observing other aerials in the street and comparing their direction. This is not so simple in a loft, so use a compass. When in the loft, keep the compass at arm's length and away from other objects (cables and metal items), otherwise a faulty reading may be given. External aerials may be moved by high winds and correction is best done by an aerial fitter.

● When a cable or connection fault is suspected, check each cable (there may be several if a video is linked) by slowly flexing them while watching the screen for an intermittent good/bad picture to appear. This should pin-point the fault in the cable.

A common problem with cables and connectors is oxidation (corrosion). If this can be cleaned off easily, do so, but fitting a new cable complete with ends may be wiser. They are readily available for DIY fitting. Take your old cable with you to ensure that you obtain the correct replacement as there are several variations. If after obtaining a new cable the fault still persists, the socket or internal connection on the set may be at fault and this will require the services of a trained television engineer.

This unit boosts a poor signal by a factor of three. It is ideal for areas with low signal strength.

DOs	DON'Ts
● Do ensure that you use the correct rating fuse. ● Do make sure that you fully understand the operating instructions by reading the manufacturer's instructions. ● Do keep children from playing with televisions, videos and other mains appliances. ● Do watch out for glass panels and doors on hi-fi equipment, which may easily be damaged. ● Do use a proper stand approved by the television manufacturer.	● Do not remove fixed panels; repair external faults only. ● Do not continue to use equipment that you suspect is faulty. Switch it off and remove the mains plug. ● Do not block the ventilation apertures on equipment with curtains, loose covers, etc. ● Do not leave equipment switched on and unattended unless you are sure it is safe to do so. ● Do not place equipment on makeshift stands. Televisions and audio items are heavy and easily damaged. Injury could also be caused.

Chapter 5

Cleaners and powertools

Vacuum cleaners

The domestic vacuum cleaner has been with us now for some 90 years, during which time it has become the most popular labour-saving appliance in the home. The basic principle of operation is quite simple. An electric motor drives fans to create a fast-moving air flow. At one end, a vacuum (suction) of air is created, while at the opposite end the air is exhausted. If the air is moved quickly enough at the inlet end, it will carry with it any debris that enters the airflow. A means of removing the debris from the airflow is required to prevent its redistribution as the air is expelled.

Over the years there have been several operational variations. The first two styles to emerge were the upright cleaner and the cylinder cleaner. The upright cleaner was designed to drive a rotating brush as well as to suck up dirt. The cylinder model cleaned purely by suction, using a flexible hose and a range of attachments. For many years, manufacturers stayed with these two basic styles, altering the design by increasing the suction power and adding refinements, such as automatic cord rewind and variable power and height settings.

Modern variations

More recently the humble vacuum cleaner has undergone more major changes. Models have been designed that combine the functions of both upright and cylinder cleaners. Some upright models even have power drive take-offs from the motor, not only for driving the revolving brush, but also to drive a clutch and gear system that powers the vacuum cleaner wheels, driving it back and forth at the lightest touch of a button. Cylinder cleaners have undergone a complete rethink and are now split into three main categories.

Redesigned suction vacuum cleaners range from simple suction only to electronic control, variable power settings and even cleaners that are self-diagnostic (a display

indicates what fault has occurred within the appliance). There is now a version with a speech processor chip that actually 'tells' you the fault!

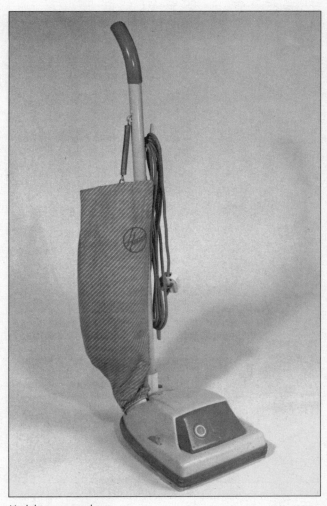

Upright vacuum cleaner.

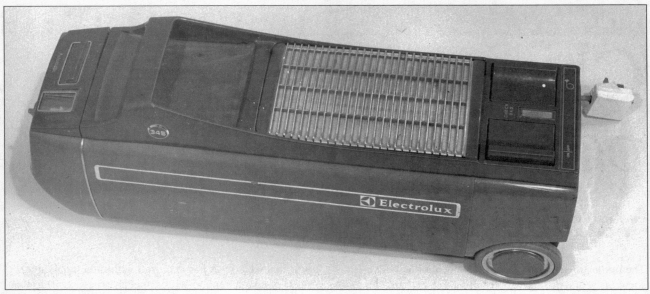

Cylinder vacuum cleaner

Three-in-one canister vacuum cleaner (with wet-and-dry facility and carpet cleaning).

Canister or bin cleaners are a domestic version of what were normally regarded as commercial machines. The greatest change has been to include the facility to vacuum up liquids: something that would in the past have damaged the appliance and created a safety hazard. The wet-and-dry operation, as it is known, has now become an option. Not all bin/canister cleaners have this option. Make sure that if a cleaner is to be used for sucking up liquids, it is designed to do so. Ordinary vacuum cleaners must not be used in wet conditions. The wet-and-dry machine must be prepared for liquid pick-up, that is, on most models specific items must be removed first to avoid damage to the appliance.

A relatively new variation of the cleaner described above combines a carpet cleaning facility with the wet-and-dry bin-type vacuum. This combination is commonly known as a 3-in-1 wet-and-dry. In addition to wet-and-dry vacuuming, it incorporates a system whereby a detergent solution from a tank is forced into the carpet or fabric and removed by suction into the main body of the vacuum. This is a fairly efficient cleaning operation that does not leave the carpet or fabric excessively damp, unlike earlier carpet shampoo machines that could not extract the soiled liquid. This function can be carried out only by a machine fitted with this feature and in most cases requires extra attachments and specialized cleaning fluids to avoid excess foaming within the tanks.

Hand-held versions of the first two types are now available. They can be mains powered, rechargeable (ni-cad battery) or 12 volt-powered for use from a car battery.

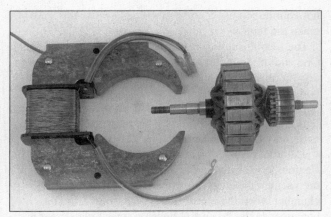

This field coil and armature are from a large Hoover upright cleaner. Individual motor parts are available for many Hoover cleaners.

Chipped and broken fans are common with this type of suction system.

Maintenance and repair

Despite the variety of shapes, sizes and makes of vacuum cleaner, they all function in much the same way and are prone to similar faults and user-handling problems.

At the heart of a vacuum cleaner there is a powerful high-speed motor. In most cases this is a series-wound brush-gear motor (see Motors, pages 28-33). This is the most versatile motor and suits this type of appliance well. It is adaptable in shape and size and capable of high speeds. Induction motors have been used in upright cleaners but their application has been restricted to one or two makes only. Small hand-held versions have motors to suit: mains-powered versions have series-wound brush motors, rechargeable (ni-cad battery) cleaners have a DC-powered permanent magnet motor and car battery types have a DC-powered series motor or a permanent magnet-type motor.

The following pages cover the repair of all types of vacuum cleaners and also advise on regular maintenance procedures to keep them in good working order. However, even with care and attention, faults will occur from time to time because of the heavy demands on these appliances. Faults fall into three categories: electrical, mechanical and misuse. The last category often has a strong link with the first two.

For ease of reference the information has been split into two sections: the upright models and cylinder/bin types. For some models reference to both sections will be required.

Upright cleaners

The upright style of vacuum cleaner is perhaps the best for large areas of carpet. It is especially good at removing dirt embedded within the pile and pet hairs from the

Many manufacturers now use plastic fans in place of metal. They are thought to be less prone to blade damage. Check that they are fitted securely to the shaft to prevent their working loose.

A typical upright vacuum cleaner motor with belt drive pulley.

surface, even on sculptured carpets. A drawback with the basic upright cleaner is its difficulty with cleaning stairs. The problem has been overcome with the modern combination of upright and cylinder cleaner. This type may be the best option if you have large areas of fitted carpet and staircases. The motor within the upright cleaner creates the airflow (suction) and drives a rotating brush roll, often called an agitator barrel.

The airflow may be produced in one of two different ways. In the first system a single fan is mounted directly on the armature end, usually by an elongated metal pulley used to drive the brush roll via a rubber belt. The fan is mounted in a housing and when rotated at high speed by the motor, creates a fast-moving airflow.

The inlet, which is positioned in such a way as to form an area of suction around the rotating brush roll, is often called the mask plate. As the fan rotates, the dirt that is picked up or loosened by the brush roll is sucked into the fan chamber and blown into a disposable paper filter bag. Although effective and used for many years, this action has a major disadvantage. All the dirt and debris picked up by the airflow comes into contact with the moving fan, resulting in chipping or wearing of the fan blades. If a large item is picked up, a blade could be completely broken off the fan. Uneven wear or slight chipping causes severe vibration and noise, resulting in poor performance or, even worse, motor bearing or motor case failure. Do

not continue to use a noisy machine because this may make the fault worse.

The second suction system avoids this kind of problem. One end of the motor's armature is extended and used to drive a brush roll via a rubber belt as before. The main body of the motor is housed in a sealed casing and the opposite end to the pulley has a series of specially shaped fans attached. When turned by the motor, they create an extremely fast movement of air.

The inlet connection of the unit is connected via a flexible tube or ducting to a sealed container or body of the vacuum cleaner. This creates a vacuum within the chamber when the motor runs. A duct runs from the container to the brush roll housing (mask plate). Air is drawn in as before, carrying any dirt and debris with it. At the entry point to the container, a disposable paper bag filter is positioned to remove the dust and debris from the airflow, simultaneously preventing it from coming into contact with the fan. Nevertheless, this system also has a drawback.

The air that flows through the sealed motor casing also cools the motor, but if the disposable bag or internal dust filters are not renewed regularly, the airflow through the system slows down or stops altogether. This not only results in poor pick-up, but in overheating of the motor. It is essential that disposable bags are renewed regularly. Filters should also be changed regularly to prevent

This motor is of the type described. One end is for the belt drive, the other end a series of fans for suction only.

This Hoover turbo motor has belt drive at one end and single fan and chamber system at the other.

further problems developing.

Repairs to faulty motors are dependent upon the manufacturer. Some supply only complete units, whereas others supply individual items as replacement spares. As a rough guide, individual parts and smaller units are usually available for cleaners that fit into the first category. Manufacturers of cleaners in the second category usually supply complete motor and fan assemblies, sometimes with motor brushes as a separate item.

The brush roll

The other main component of the upright cleaner is the brush roll. It is turned by a drive from the end of the motor, creating a sweeping and beating action. This lifts the carpet pile to clean thoroughly. If a beating action is incorporated, there will be a bar on the barrel in place of one brush row. It vibrates grit from the pile base to the surface where it can be sucked up by the airflow and removed. This may sound a rough operation, but all it involves is the mask plate lifting the carpet slightly away from the floor and the beater bar tapping the carpet to free the grit embedded within the pile.

Removing grit particles is extremely beneficial. If they are left, movement on the surface, such as someone walking on it, causes the grit to wear through the base of the pile. Doorways and passageways are particularly likely areas for this problem. A loss of pile is often blamed on a poor carpet when, in fact, poor cleaning by an inefficient or unsuitable vacuum cleaner is the main cause.

The brush roll belt may be round or flat depending on the style of cleaner. Many sizes of belts are available, but it is essential that only the one for your particular model is used. Using the wrong size belt causes damage to the motor and brush roll bearings. Various qualities are also available, but cheap copies may prove not to be cost effective because they have a tendency to break frequently or, due to overheating, shed black residue on to your carpets.

The brush roll is supported on bearings at each end so the barrel rotates freely. Types of bearings, barrels and brushes differ from model to model as well as between manufacturers. Some manufacturers supply individual parts for the brush roll, such as brush strips, bearings and barrel; others supply only complete assemblies. The brush roll on some models may have removable brush strips, whereas others may be a solid brush roll of wood or plastic with fixed brushes. A small selection is shown here to highlight the differences.

The end bearings are of one of two types: small ball race or simple sleeve bearing. The first is prone to dust penetration causing noise or seizure of the brush roll. Cleaning and regreasing regularly will alleviate any serious problems. Sleeve bearings are also prone to dirt penetration, but although regular lubrication does help, often the shaft of the brush roll wears or the sleeve bearing hole becomes elongated by the constant pull of the belt drive. This type of problem causes the brush roll to stop rotating, resulting in poor pick-up and frequent belt renewal. In this instance, the belt acts like a fuse or weak link. If the brush roll is jammed or slow running, the motor continues to turn although in a laboured way.

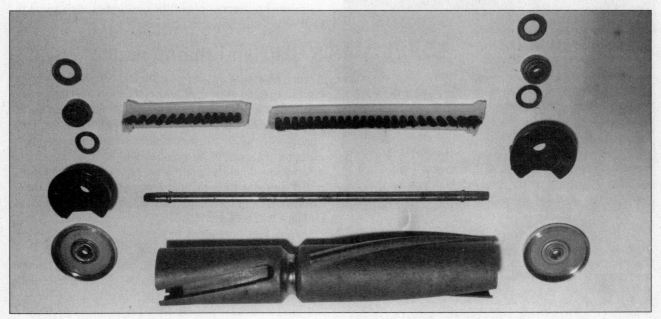

Typical brush roll components Each part of this roll is available separately or it can be bought as a complete unit.

of the hose, it may be necessary to remove the actual hose end if possible. In most instances, reversing the airflow through the hose frees the blockage.

Wet-and-dry models

Appliances suitable for wet-and-dry operation look like ordinary cylinder/canister cleaners, but the internal design, which incorporates a ball-type floating valve, is quite different. The valve mechanically closes the inlet (suction) point to the motor from the dirt/liquid container if an excess of water is drawn into it.

The operation of this valve is simple yet effective. The increase in water level lifts the ball from its normal position closer to the inlet (suction) duct. When close enough, the suction lifts the ball into the inlet and effectively seals it to prevent water from being drawn into the motor compartment. This action also prevents any further liquid being drawn into the container. It is essential that the ball moves freely within its housing at all times.

There are both earthed and double insulated versions of this appliance. It is most important to follow the manufacturer's instructions and reposition all parts correctly.

Three-in-one machines

The basic operation of this machine is identical to the wet-and-dry type. However, it incorporates a tank for a water and detergent mixture which can be fed as required to a special cleaning head, thus combining carpet shampooing with dirty water extraction.

The tank which holds the detergent and water is pressurized by a feed from the motor exhaust. A tube runs

Ball valve system of wet-and-dry machine.

from below the liquid level of the tank to a control valve on the end of the vacuum hose. When cleaning solution is required, the valve is opened and the solution from the tank is forced along the tube to the cleaning head. The solution is then fed into the pile of the carpet and as the head is moved over the surface, the now dirty liquid is sucked into the lower container via the normal suction hose. An alternative to this is the jet system which supplies the cleaning head with solution at a higher pressure via a small pump unit.

Warning

To use appliances for wet-and-dry or shampooing requires the fitting or removing of certain parts specific to each model. It is not possible to list all the variations here, so reference should be made to the manufacturer's instructions before carrying out any of these operations. Specialized cleaning fluids are required for use with these products. They usually have anti-foaming agents to prevent foam and water penetration of the motor unit. It is advisable to use only the products approved for use in these appliances; failure to do so could cause damage or create a safety hazard. Ensure that the machine is cleaned thoroughly after wet-and-dry operation or shampooing, because dirty liquids and detergent deposits can cause build-ups or blockages during normal use.

Cord rewinds

Cord rewinds are now found on all types of cleaners, from simple hand-operated versions to the fully automatic rewind at the touch of a button. Many auto cord rewind systems use open coil springs and great care should be exercised if a stripdown of these systems is called for. Protection for the eyes is recommended. Goggles afford adequate protection from the spring itself or any item that it may throw out in the event of its slipping from position.

Operation of the cord rewind relies on tensioning of the rewind spring as the cord is pulled out for use. A small brake pad prevents the immediate return of the spring and cord drum to its original position. When the rewind button or lever is pressed, the brake is released and the drum is rotated by the spring, pulling in the cord as it does so. To ensure that all the cord is returned to the drum, the spring has a degree of tension left at the end of the cord travel (usually four turns). This is why you should take care when removing or servicing this item. The main reason why you will need to gain access to or remove the cord rewind is to renew a damaged cable which is common at the entry point of the cable on the drum centre (see pages 160-161).

A suitable replacement flex must be obtained. It must

be sufficiently flexible to coil easily on to the drum and be of the same length as the one that is being replaced. Ensure all cord grips are fitted correctly and that the moving contact points are not bent or damaged. Renew any burnt or damaged rings or contacts. Note the positions of all items at each stage of the stripdown.

'Bag full' indicators

Found mainly on cylinder models, the 'bag full' indicator ought to be a useful device. Unfortunately, all too often it is ignored and eventually it fails, sticking and giving an inaccurate indication.

The visual indicator operates by moving a coloured piston/slide against a spring. The bag indicator unit has a small bleed hole or slot that allows air into the compartment via the slide/piston unit. In normal circumstances, air is easily drawn in through the bag and hose. When these are choked or blocked, thus producing a greater vacuum in the compartment, more air is pulled through the indicator inlet. The increase in air movement progressively pushes on the piston/slide overcoming the resistance of the spring, giving an indication of the degree of blockage or how nearly full the bag is.

Problems arise if dirt is drawn into the bleed hole or slot and jams the piston or slide, resulting in a false reading. With care, most can be easily removed for cleaning. Ensure that all parts are free to move. Testing is quite simple. With the machine in its normal state and ready for use (hose connected, no attachments fitted), turn the cleaner on and intermittently cover the end of the hose with the palm of your hand while observing the indicator window. The indicator should move across from one side to the other as your hand first covers, then uncovers the open end of the hose. There are some

variations, but the basic principle is the same. Carry out this simple test regularly in order to check that the indicator is working correctly.

Disposable bags and filters

It is easy to dismiss the disposable bag as just a receptacle in which the dirt is collected during cleaning. However, there is a little more to it than that. Many faults can be directly attributed to infrequent bag renewal or the use of poor quality bags and filters.

To work correctly, the bag must offer as little resistance to the airflow as possible, even as its contents increase. It must also resist clogging, while at the same time stopping fine particles from passing through. Restriction to the airflow through the bag and filter not only results in poor cleaning performance, but may cause premature motor failure as a result of overheating.

Porosity – the ability to let air through but retain dust and dirt – has to be matched to the bag size and motor power for each model. Because the bag is made of paper or 'non-woven fabric' it might be thought that any paper bag would do. This is not so. Unfortunately, there are many bags available that purport to be suitable for particular models at much lower cost than the genuine replacements. The price of many genuine bags tends to push the cost-conscious into buying the cheaper alternative brands. If not chosen carefully, the cheaper bags could eventually be the cause of an expensive complete motor renewal.

There are some excellent quality bags available that do match the original specifications. With a little effort, these bags can be identified and they usually cost somewhere between the low price of the inferior bags and the higher price of the bags marked as genuine. Few

A cord rewind may be found on many machines, both cylinder and upright.

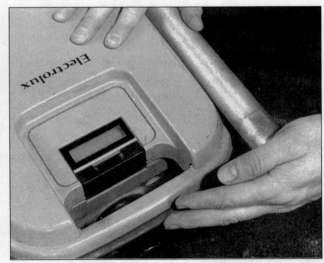

Test the 'bag full' indicator by blocking the hose end with your hand.

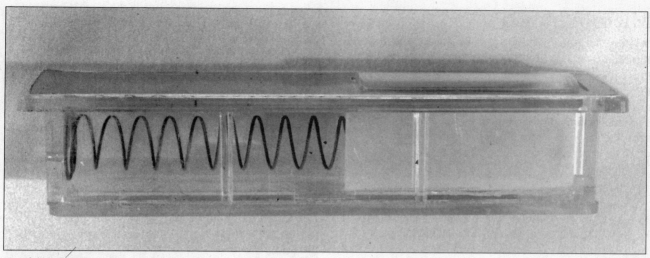

'Bag full' indicator – spring and slide type.

appliance manufacturers produce all their own bags. They are made by specialized companies and then given the manufacturer's trademark. The same bag manufacturer may produce bags of the same quality to be sold under different brand name but without the appliance manufacturer's mark-up.

There are a few tests you can carry out to indicate bag quality. First, check for porosity by covering your mouth with a section of the new paper bag and exhale. You should feel little resistance as the air should pass through easily. Next, check the seams and sealed ends of the bag. Look for secure double folding and strong gluing; many problems are caused by bags coming apart when full.

Some bags are designed to have an open end which is secured by a clip, allowing the bag to be emptied and reused. It is advisable to reuse a bag only once as fine dust blocks the pores of the filter paper. Better still, avoid the mess and inconvenience of emptying the bag, and use a fresh one each time. This will also help keep the cleaning action at peak performance. Reusable cloth bags are available, but are not recommended for the same reasons. Fine dust is difficult to remove from the weave, suction and airflow is impaired and they tend to smell if not thoroughly cleaned and washed regularly. Inspect the inner of the bag for many cylinder cleaners use double-wall bags (two layers of filter) to increase filtration and remove tiny dust particles often missed with cheap poor quality bags.

Ensure that bags with cardboard apertures fit correctly. Some use a rubber membrane, so if the original had one, the replacement bag must also have one. The bag must be a secure fit otherwise dust and dirt will bypass the bag and clog secondary filters or, worse still, enter the motor. Bags that are poorly fitted are often only spotted once the damage has been done, so check first to avoid problems.

This cleaner has three types of filter: disposable bag, secondary filter and exhaust filter.

Micro-filtration

The advent of double-wall bags has greatly improved the filtration standards of disposable bags by reducing the recirculation of very fine dust that single-wall bags allow through. The use of double-wall bags creates a micro-filtration effect which is both beneficial to the appliance and the household environment in general. To keep such a system operating efficiently, change disposable bags and secondary filters regularly.

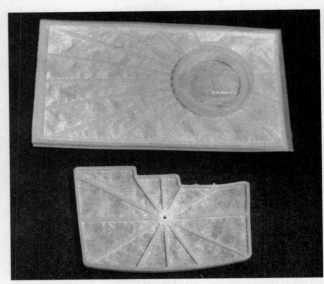

There are many varieties of plastic framed secondary filters. Regular renewal is essential.

Cylinder cleaner repair

This pear-shaped cylinder cleaner does not work at all. First check the socket and plug. If these are all right, suspect a cable or internal fault. Isolate the cleaner and begin checking.

1 All the functional parts of this type of cleaner – switch, motor, cord rewind – are housed in the rear compartment. The fixing screws are not immediately visible.

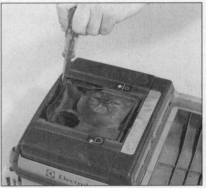

2 Lift and remove the exhaust cover and filter and look for two hidden screws towards the rear. Remove these and take off the rear panel.

3 There are no obvious fixing screws to the front section, but it is likely that some form of fixing lies beneath the metal trim in the centre. Ease this carefully from its position.

4 Removing the metal trim reveals two special fixing screws. An old flat-bladed screwdriver can be modified for removing them.

5 Remove the cord rewind pedal and the switch pedal. They both have loose return springs and plastic retaining clips.

6 You can now gain access to the main compartment by removing five cross-head screws and lifting the top cover carefully.

7 Test all the circuit for continuity. Leap-frog testing traced the problem to a loose connection on the motor. Tightening and refitting is all that is required.

Had the fault been within the motor it would have required the fitting of a complete motor and fan unit because individual motor parts are not available. Clean the compartment and motor thoroughly before reassembly. Double-check all work carried out and then reassembly is a straightforward reversal of the stripdown sequence. Take care to fit all fixings correctly. Fit a new inner and exhaust filter before the functional test

Cord rewind repair

This cylinder cleaner does not work at all. Isolate the machine and begin checking. If the plug and socket proved all right, suspect a cable or internal fault. Access to this conventional looking cylinder cleaner is much easier.

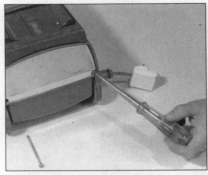

1 Remove the two recessed cross-head screws so that the cord rewind unit can be removed.

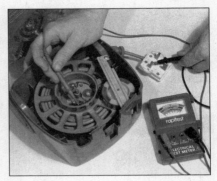

2 Test for continuity. An open circuit is found between the plug and the rewind contact on the neutral side. (The neon may still light even with an open circuit neutral return.)

3 Open circuit faults near to the centre entry point are common on rewinds. This is due to constant movement. At first sight, the fault may not be apparent but here the cable is obviously damaged.

If the rest of the flex is in good condition, all that may be required is to remove the first section of flex just in front of the fault and reconnect to the rewind assembly. In most instances, however, it is best to fit a new length of flex. Buy a cable of suitable quality and identical to the original specification, that is in flexibility, length and diameter (it is quite possible that the colour may not match). Some cable may not be flexible enough for use on rewind systems; check when purchasing.

4 Wear goggles when removing the cable drum to protect yourself from the coiled spring. Remove the plug and allow the rewind to fully coil the spring back before its removal.

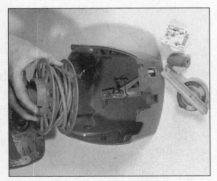

5 With the spring removed, press the cord release lever and ease the drum out of its position to expose the braking system below. Fit the new flex to the drum.

6 Check that the braking system is correctly positioned when refitting the drum by pressing the brake release to allow the drum to seat correctly.

7 Check that the drum is fitted in exactly the same way as the original and that all cable clamps and covers are fitted correctly.

8 With drum and the new cable positioned correctly, fit the cord stop to the cable. Carefully refit the spring. Run four turns around the drum centre before securing the spring on its mount. (This allows a good return on the whole length of flex.)

9 With all parts correctly fitted, double-check all work and fit the plug to the cable end.

10 Make a further continuity check of the motor circuit. The motor used in this machine is the same as that shown in the previous stripdown. Access to it is by removing the four cross-head screws in each corner of the inner plastic housing.
This allows the housing to be removed giving access to the motor unit. Refitting the unit is a reversal of the stripdown procedure. Functional testing should be carried out using an RCD protected circuit.

Power tools

There is what seems to be an ever-increasing range of labour-saving equipment capable of tackling the wide variety of repair and building work now taken on by the DIY home-owner. Tools that were once used in only professional workshops and factories are now quite commonplace around the house. Electric drills, routers, grinders, saws and planes are now produced to meet the demand from the rapidly increasing army of DIY enthusiasts. The diversity and range available is vast. They are all based on an electric motor taking the place of manual effort. Each has a powerful motor for direct drive or reduction via a gearbox or electronic control and can be found in mains or battery powered versions in most instances.

Maintenance and repair

Many of the faults with power tools are common to all appliances with electric motors. At the heart of these tools there is a brush motor (see Motors, pages 28-33) and when mains powered, a supply cable is also present. These are the two areas where most faults occur – misuse and neglect accounting for a large proportion of them. It must be stressed that these types of appliances are extremely powerful and great care must be taken when using them. Each piece of equipment has a limit to its capabilities, so a sound understanding of its function and operation will be of enormous benefit to the user and the equipment itself.

Regular maintenance avoids unnecessary faults and the safe use of both electricity and equipment avoids injury caused by ignorance. Always read the manufacturer's instructions carefully. If you are borrowing equipment, make sure that you understand the correct use and limitations of the product and that you have the proper safety wear. When lending your equipment to someone else, ensure the borrower fully understands how to use the various tools safely.

Personal safety

The use of an RCD is highly recommended when you are using power tools because it affords an important extra degree of electrical protection. It is absolutely vital for outdoor work. Problems with water and cable damage can happen to anyone at any time, so it is wise to be prepared. Even with an RCD, mains powered equipment should not be used in damp or wet conditions.

Do not change drill bits, cutters or other attachments without first isolating the appliance; do not rely on the on/off switch alone. Switch off and take the plug out. Always ensure the fixing tool – Allen key, chuck key, spanner, etc. – used for changing attachments has been removed before the equipment is used. Double-check. Remember, too, when tightening the chuck of a drill to do so at all three positions and not just one.

Do not use drills or attachments that are too large or not suited to the drill. Do not exceed the maximum bit (shaft) size. If a speed control is available, use it correctly. The smaller the drill, the faster the speed can be; larger drill bits require slower speeds. Use a hammer action only when drilling masonry.

Hold the drill securely and do not overstress it. Remember, if a drill or attachment jams, the body of the drill will try to rotate and if it is not held securely, the torque produced could cause injury. If the drill has an

Jig saw.

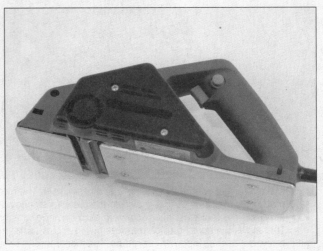

Plane.

Chain saw.

Basic safety equipment includes goggles, mask and ear protectors or plugs.

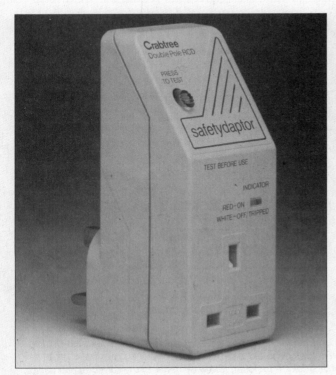

An RCD is essential.

additional grip handle (often removable), use it.

Do not cover the air vents on the body of the appliance with your hands or anything else to try to prevent excess dust or dirt entering it. Many attachments allow for vacuum dust extraction. Using such equipment will not only cut down the mess, it will be healthier for the user.

Never leave equipment plugged in and unattended, even if it is switched off. Always store equipment safely and tidily when not in use. Never carry any appliance by its mains lead as this will cause excessive wear and damage. When the job is finished, allow the motor and attachments to come to rest before putting the appliance down; otherwise damage to property or personal injury could result.

Ensure that safety covers and guards are working correctly. Appliances with cracked cases or missing parts should not be used until they have been properly repaired. Make sure that any items to be drilled, cut or ground are securely anchored. Keep your area free from clutter and keep both children and pets at a safe distance.

Take care in garages and workshops where fuel vapour may collect. Using power tools in these areas can ignite the mixture by the normal spark/arcing of the motor brushes. Ventilate thoroughly before using power tools and do not use in places where vapours may be present.

Before using any power tools check the mains lead along its whole length for any damage and verify that the on/off switch works correctly and is not sticking. Remember also that tidy work areas are safer work areas. Do not use power tools in cluttered or cramped conditions.

Safety with power saws

There are several types of power saws; using any of them requires great care and vigilance. Two types in particular call for extreme caution because they are subject to an undesirable characteristic known as 'kick-back'. This occurs when an obstacle or poorly secured workpiece jams the saw – usually momentarily. The inertia can easily pull the equipment from the hands even when held firmly. The injuries that result from uncontrolled kick-back can be very dangerous.

Both circular and chain saws are prone to kick-back if used incorrectly. Read the manufacturer's instructions thoroughly before using either and wear protective clothing.

Hand-held circular saws

● Make sure that all safety guards are in good order and working correctly.
● Fit the correct blade for the job and check it is secure. Make sure that it runs true (is not buckled) and has no

teeth missing.
- Firmly clamp the item to be cut.
- Grip the saw firmly and adopt a well-balanced posture, ensuring that there are no obstacles to trip over in the vicinity.
- Move cables or any other items well clear of the blade before switching on.
- After switching on, allow the blade to reach full speed before starting the cut.
- Do not force the cut or you will move off line and this is how kick-back can happen. Take it slowly and concentrate.
- When the cut is finished, switch off and allow the blade to stop before removing it from the workpiece or putting the saw down.
- Remember to remove the plug between use and keep other people at a safe distance.

Chain saws

The possibility of kick-back from a chain saw is greater than from a circular saw. Chain saws are not suitable for general woodwork; their main function is felling trees and cutting branches into logs. As this is obviously outdoor work, all the previously mentioned safety rules should be followed along with a few extra ones.
- Protection should include goggles, gloves, ear defenders and stout footwear.

- Keep a firm grip with both hands at all times.
- The workpiece must be held securely. If lopping branches from trees, do not make cuts on the undersides of branches as they will close up, trapping the saw, resulting in kick-back or damage to the equipment.
- Take up a well-balanced stance on firm ground before starting to cut.
- Never use the saw above waist height.
- Check the on/off switch is working correctly and the cable is safe.
- Allow the saw to reach full speed before starting the cut.
- Keep other people and pets at a safe distance, although it is wise to have someone at hand in case something goes wrong.
- When the cut is finished let the saw stop completely before putting it down.
- Do not forget to unplug the saw between use.

Reciprocating saws

This type of saw is not prone to kick-back. It produces a double action sawing movement via a gear box. It is much easier and safer to use although safety precautions must still be taken to secure the workpiece. It is much more adaptable than circular or chain saws. Also it has provision for attaching a range of different types of

The hot air gun is similar in operation to a hairdryer although the heat output is much higher. Keep all such equipment away from children and use only for the tasks for which they are specifically designed. If you are removing old lead-based paints, wear a protective mask to avoid breathing the fumes and toxic dust. This also applies to others in the vicinity. If in doubt, it may be better to use solvent-based paint removers to prevent the possibility of inhaling lead-laden fumes or dust.

This internal view of a mains powered electric drill shows clearly the large brush gear motor and gearbox drive.

blades for cutting wood, thermal building blocks, pipe
work, plastics and composite laminates.
● Hold the saw firmly.
● Move cables and other items clear of the cutting area.
● Do not use a reciprocating saw above shoulder height.
● Take up a safe working position and a firm stance
before switching on.
● Adjust your position according to the work to be
carried out.

Motors

The motors used in power tools are very similar to those
used in vacuum cleaners and mixers. Appliances with
electronic variable speed control functions also operate in
the same way. One exception is the gearbox-type speed
control (usually with only two available speeds). These
act in a purely mechanical way by changing the drive
gearing, similar to a car gear box. A list of typical fault
symptoms follows. It should be used in conjunction with
the motor information in Motors (pages 28-33), Vacuum
cleaners (pages 137-162) and Mixers (pages 100-107).

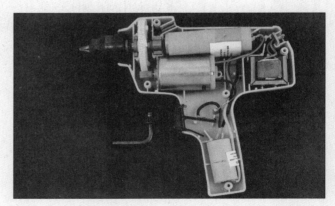

*Removing five securing screws on this cordless power screwdriver
enabled the casing to split. The small but powerful motor, simple
gear system and battery packs can be seen clearly. The transformer
on the far right shows that a separate charger is not used as it is
mounted internally.*

POWER TOOLS
WATCHPOINTS

1   **Plan your work before starting** – stop and think.

2   **Use an RCD,** especially for work outdoors.

3   **Do not use power tools in wet or damp conditions.**

4   **Fit a resilient plug** to all portable power appliances.

5   **Do not change attachments without unplugging** the appliance.

6   **Hold the handle of power tools securely;** if there is a grip, use it.

7   **Wear all-round goggles** to protect your eyes when using such tools as drills, grinders and routers.

8   **Wear a mask** with a suitable filter as protection against fine dust.

9   **Switch off** immediately if a fault or problem occurs. Unplug the appliance.

Power tool repair

This drill operates slowly and intermittently.

1 Remove the five screws to allow the casing to be split. This provides good access to all parts. Note the position of all parts and correct wiring routes.

2 Check the front bearing. While holding the unit firmly, grip the chuck and check for excessive movement signifying bearing or shaft wear.

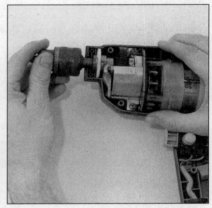

3 Check the gears by rotating the chuck. Look for excessive wear, damaged teeth and lack of lubrication.

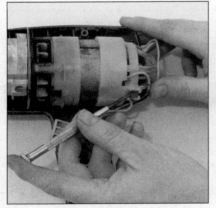

4 Remove the motor brushes with a small screwdriver and inspect them carefully.

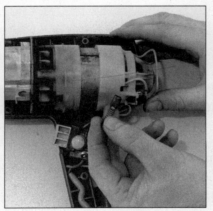

5 The fault in this case is in the brush. Clean the brush slides with a cotton bud. Buy and fit a new set of motor brushes.

6 Before refitting the outer cover, make a final double-check that all parts and wiring are in their original positions. Carry out a functional test using an RCD protected circuit.

Fault finder

Symptom: Will not work at all

POSSIBLE CAUSE	ACTION
Faulty plug or socket.	See Plugs and sockets (pages 12-21).
Fault in flex.	See Cables (pages 22-25) and Electrical circuit testing (pages 44-47). Renew as required.
Internal wiring open circuit.	Check continuity; see Electrical circuit testing (pages 44-47). This also applies to charging unit on battery versions. Many charging units are sealed and cannot be repaired. Check that all other tests prove all right and renew if suspect.
Motor brush worn/sticking.	See page 165, Motors (pages 28-33) and Electrical circuit testing (pages 44-47).
Faulty on/off switch.	See Electrical circuit testing (pages 44-47).
Open circuit TOC or overheat protective device in motor (if fitted).	Check for continuity; see Temperature control devices (pages 40-43) and Electrical circuit testing (pages 44-47).
Fault in electronic speed control unit (if applicable).	Double-check all other items thoroughly. If they are all right, obtain replacement control and retest.
Low charge.	Recharge and retest.

Symptom: Excessive noise

POSSIBLE CAUSE	ACTION
Dirt or debris on motor or cooling fan.	Strip and clean motor and inner casing.
Motor bearings worn.	Check for worn armature shaft/loose bearing. Check sideways movement and free running of bearing.
Gearbox wear/lubrication.	Check gear teeth and bearings. Lubricate as required.
Main driveshaft bearing.	Check for worn shaft or loose bearing. Renew as required.

Symptom: Body gets excessively hot

POSSIBLE CAUSE	ACTION
Vent holes blocked or covered during use.	Check correct positioning of hands during use. If all right, check vents internally. Clean as required.
Battery short-circuited (battery versions).	Correct short circuits and renew batteries as they will have been damaged.
Motor short-circuited/overheated.	Check for overheated or short-circuited coil or armature.

Symptom: Motor runs slowly or is sluggish

POSSIBLE CAUSE	ACTION
Carbon brushes worn or sticking in slides.	Check length of brushes and for free movement within holders. Mark the brush position before removing to ensure they are refitted the same way around. Renew both springs and brushes if worn. Check commutator for wear or damage.
Faulty commutator or armature windings.	Inspect commutator for signs of excessive wear, overheating, loose segments, short circuited windings or catching on field coil when rotated. If faulty, renew armature and brushes. Not all makes allow for individual part replacement. In some instances only a complete motor drive is obtainable.
Worn armature bearings.	Check armature for sideways movement. This allows the armature to be pulled on to the field coil when the motor runs.
Loose or defective field coil catching on armature.	Check field coil securing screws or clips. Reposition and tighten if possible.
Gearbox or chuck drive bearing faults.	Inspect gearbox and drive for bearing wear. Renew parts or lubricate as required.
Open circuit TOC or overheat protective device in motor (if fitted). .	Check for continuity. See Temperature control devices (pages 40-43) and Electrical circuit testing (pages 44-47).
Insufficient charge on ni-cad batteries or ageing batteries (battery versions only).	Recharge for correct length of time. Check internal wiring for open circuit. If these and all other checks prove all right, renew all batteries with correct rechargeable replacements.

Symptom: Intermittent operation

POSSIBLE CAUSE	ACTION
Poor internal connection to battery, motor or switch.	Check continuity and all joints and wiring.
Check mains lead for wear or intermittent open circuit.	See Cables (pages 22-25) and Electrical circuit testing (pages 44-47).
Sticking motor brush.	Remove, clean or renew as required.

All of the above checks and tests, except functional testing to verify correct or incorrect operation, must be carried out with the appliances isolated: switch off, plug out. When carrying out a functional test, make sure all cables and wiring have been fitted back into their correct positions. Any parts renewed must be identical to the original specification. Quote model and serial numbers when obtaining spare parts.

Garden power tools

This chapter is closely related to the previous chapter on DIY power tools which, in some areas of operation, overlap. Some power tools have attachments for garden work. The use of electrically powered machinery requires the most scrupulous safety observance. In this and many other aspects, DIY power tools and garden power tools are alike.

Like DIY power tools, a brush gear motor is used to power garden equipment, whether mower, trimmer or weeder. Both mains and battery (rechargeable) versions are available. A similarity to vacuum cleaner motors has already been noted and this also applies to the garden equipment. This is evident from the illustrations of the hover mower (see page 172). The motor has more than a passing resemblance to one of the cylinder cleaner motors featured in the chapter on vacuum cleaners (see pages 137-162). As there are so many similarities, the operation of the motor is not described again here. However, information about common faults and maintenance is, of course, included.

Proper maintenance is most important for items used outdoors in harsh conditions and often stored for long periods between uses. Prevention is better than cure; cleaning and sensible storage will help reduce the possibility of serious faults. If a fault should occur during use, switch off the equipment immediately and remove the plug from the mains supply. Do not attempt to inspect the equipment until it is completely isolated.

When purchasing garden power tools, make sure that they are suitable for the task. Overtaxing a piece of equipment that is not suited to the job causes all sorts of problems and often leads to personal injury. Choosing the right equipment is important. Repair and maintenance cannot make equipment work satisfactorily if the conditions are totally unsuitable in the first place, so seek the advice of experts before buying.

Read the manufacturer's instructions thoroughly and make sure you fully understand the capabilities and, especially, the limitations of your appliance – if possible before buying, and certainly before use.

Safety

It is sensible to follow both the general rules for safety (see Safety guide, pages 2-4) and those specifically concerned with power tools (see Power tools, pages 162-163). There are also additional considerations that apply to garden power tools.

● Do not use mains powered tools or extension leads in wet grass or in damp conditions.

When cleaning, inspecting or repairing equipment, always make sure that it is isolated: switch off, plug out.

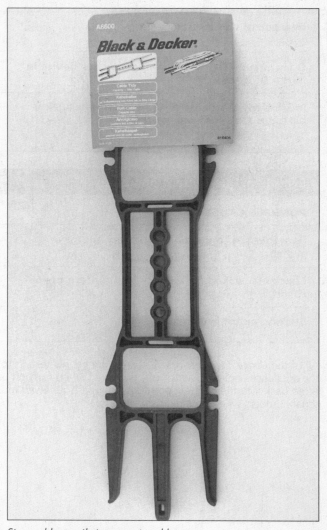

Store cables neatly to prevent problems.

Keep air vents clear of debris.

Ensure the item is isolated and clean the equipment after each use. Do not store dirty or wet equipment.

- Always wear sturdy shoes or boots when using a lawn mower. Wear goggles and gloves when using a hedge trimmer or nylon strimmer.
- Take extra care when mowing on uneven ground. Never mow up steep slopes and do not pull a hover mower towards you.
- Check the area to be mown for debris (stones, twigs, toys, etc.) as they may damage the mower and cause personal injury.
- Do not lift or move a mower of any description if the blades or cylinder are still rotating. Always switch off and unplug first.
- When using a hedge trimmer, do not tackle branches that are too thick for your particular cutting head. Always make sure the cable is safely positioned before commencing cutting. Drape the flex over your shoulder and down your back but remember to allow enough flex so that movement is not impeded.
- Always allow the motor to reach full speed before starting to cut and do not over-reach.
- Remember, safety applies both to you and to others. Do not be distracted when using equipment, but be aware of any possible danger areas (pavements, borders, clothes lines, etc.) and take measures to avoid them.

Always use equipment on an RCD-protected circuit or an RCD adapter.

This cylinder mower switch unit has an overload switch (TOC) that requires manual resetting should it trip. The positioning of the switch can vary with different models. Not all electric mowers are fitted with an overload protection.

Tripping of the TOC can be for any number of reasons: use in unsuitable conditions, continual use over a long period of time and jamming, for example. When tripping occurs, unplug the equipment and take a little time to assess the cause of the problem. The motor could overheat if the equipment is used over a long period of time in unsuitable conditions. If so, allow a time for cooling. If jamming is the cause, isolate, remove any debris, then check to see if any damage has been caused to any parts.

Hover mower repair

The hover action is a reversal of the vacuum cleaner system. It is the expelled air that is used to create lift. Blocking of the air flow will reduce lift and cause the motor to overheat. As with the vacuum cleaner motor, internal faults usually require a complete motor. A little care and attention, however, can help reduce motor failure.

TOOLS AND MATERIALS

- ☐ Screwdriver
- ☐ Small soft brush
- ☐ Spanner
- ☐ Cutting blade (New safety type)

1 This hover mower has had little or no maintenance. Although it works, it produces poor results and is very noisy. The air intake vents are badly blocked by grass cuttings Thorough cleaning of the whole machine is needed.

2 Remove the four screws from the corners and take off the top cover. This exposes an inner cover that is a push fit only.

3 Remove the inner cover to provide access to the motor. This also requires a thorough cleaning. The state of the wiring on this mower is as a result of poor positioning from a previous repair. It is sensible to correct this before fault tracing.

4 Carefully and thoroughly clean the motor and then inspect it for faults and loose connections caused by vibration.

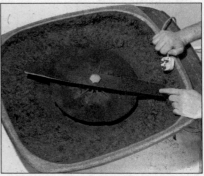

5 With the mower upturned, the cause of the vibration can be seen. The cutting blade is badly damaged (due to careless use).

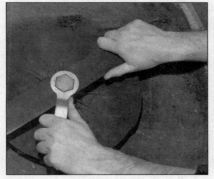

6 Clean the mower and remove the damaged blade. Check the motor bearings for excessive movement. In this instance, they are all right.

7 Fit a new safety blade. Out of balance blades create vibration, so it is advisable to check all electrical connections as they may have been loosened by the vibration.

Double-check all connections and work carried out before replacing the covers and making a functional test.

Cylinder mower typical fault

This mower regularly trips the overload TOC even during short periods of use. A thorough stripdown must be carried out to identify the cause.

TOOLS AND MATERIALS

- ☐ Screwdriver(s)
- ☐ Socket and ratchet
- ☐ Bearing
- ☐ Spanner
- ☐ Small soft brush

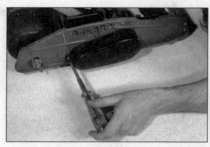

1 Isolate the equipment and remove the screw securing the plastic belt cover.

2 Remove the belt cover and ease the belt off the pulley.

3 To remove the large drive pulley, jam the cylinder and turn the pulley to unscrew it from the shaft. Remove the rear/drive pulley securing bolt with a socket and ratchet and pull from the shaft.

4 Ease the cylinder bearing securing clip out of position by lifting the spring steel points with a small screwdriver.

5 Remove the bearing spacer and spring washer. Note the position of each item and lay them out in order to ensure correct refitting. In this instance a new bearing is required due to wear.

6 Remove all the screws securing the side panel. Note their correct positions and lay them out tidily.

7 Slacken the cutting plate adjustment nut to allow the motor and end frame to be removed. Note items' positions, especially the spring washer to the base of the adjusting rod and the filter/grille cover.

Thoroughly clean internal parts of the motor compartment. Reassembly is a direct reversal of the stripdown procedure, taking care that all parts are refitted into their original positions. A similar but simpler stripdown is then carried out on the other side, where there is a further build-up of debris. As stated earlier, new cylinder bearings are required.

8 Two problem areas in this mower are apparent. The motor air filters are blocked and a solid build-up of grass has formed on the cylinder shaft to the rear of the bearing. This acts as a brake and, combined with poor cooling of the motor, has resulted in overload.